My Struggle

First published in the UK in 1995 by
Boxtree Limited
Broadwall House
21 Broadwall
London SE1 9PL

24681097531

Designed by Blackjacks
Visual Imaging by Scanners
Photography by Paul Forrester and Laura Wickenden
Archive photographs – Hulton Deutsch
Circus poster by kind permission of Mary Evans Picture Library
Printed and bound in Great Britain by
The Bath Press, Avon

ISBN 0 7522 0775 X

A CIP catalogue entry for this book is
available from the British Library

PAUL MERTON
My Struggle

BXTREE

Editor's Foreword

Working in publishing isn't all paperbacks and wine-bars I can assure you. It's a tough, cut-throat business and the casualty rate is high. As a commissioning editor I have to decide which books to publish and more importantly when to publish them. A colleague of mine once made a terrible mistake by launching an entire series of 1987 Horoscope Guides in 1991. As in most things worth doing, timing is of the essence.

In my time at Boxtree I have received many unsolicited manuscripts. Some have been badly typed, others have been written in pencil. But never in my fifteen years experience have I received a package that resembled the one that landed on my desk on July 9th 1995. A scruffy brown envelope stuffed with a lot of old photographs and also containing a single cassette tape. On another day I might well have thrown the whole lot straight into a waste paper basket. Luckily the office waste paper baskets had been removed that very morning to undergo their annual service and a literary masterpiece was saved from immediate destruction.

I admit that the name Paul Merton didn't mean very much to me. Perhaps a vague memory of a quiz show that he may have been involved with a long time ago but nothing more than that. So I listened to the tape expecting the usual tired old anecdotes that one normally associates with showbiz memoirs. But what I heard was a revelation.

For the first time ever the inner workings of show-business have been exposed for exactly what they are. Sensational, malevolent, patronising, unbelievable and above all criminal. This book lays bare the torment behind the glittering facade. Some of it isn't pretty but then the truth is often like that.

I must thank the author's mother Mrs Mary Merton for kindly sending in the material in the first place and I hope she is pleased with the finished results. All efforts to contact Paul Merton however have proved futile. I have been unable to find his phone number or his home address. He seems to have disappeared from the face of the earth. Frankly it doesn't surprise me. A lot of very powerful people will be furious that this book has been published and Paul would do well to keep his head down. The rest of us all owe him something for his outstanding efforts in detailing the true nature of show-business. If you've ever wondered what lies behind the tear in a clown's eye then read on.

Jake Lingwood
BOXTREE September 1995

Chapter 1

Testing, testing. One two, one, two! Right . . .

The Merton Dynasty has been involved in showbusiness since the late 1790s. My great-grandfather was Henry Merton, a noted circus performer in his prime who in later years became a very successful promoter and founded the unique Merton's Travelling Circus. It was unique in that unlike other circuses it actually travelled while the audience were inside the tent watching the show. By linking the Big Top via sturdy chains to thirty-five palomino horses the entire circus was capable of travelling up to seventeen miles an hour during an evening's performance. At the end of the night the happy crowds would emerge from the Big Top and discover much to their amusement that they had no idea where they were or how to get home. Some didn't even bother and simply settled into their new surroundings, happy in the knowledge that they were meeting new people. Once word got around about this fascinating gimmick some enterprising folk used it to their advantage. If a farmer wanted to take his pigs to market but didn't fancy the five-mile walk, he would buy front row seats for himself and his pigs and then leave during the interval. Provided he'd timed it properly he would

Travelling Circus Device V 1 trapeze (estimated speed of about 15 mph)

tightrope big top

bit of wood elephant

wheel chairs (cots)

horses (30 or 40 should do)

chains

horses take it in turns to walk backwards or forwards

find himself just a few short yards from his intended destination.

Business was so good for Henry that by 1849 he had a fleet of Big Tops criss-crossing the country. For the first time the great majority of people were experiencing the joys of travel. The system had endless advantages. If a family of four turned up late for a matinée performance only to discover that the circus had already left town, they wouldn't be too disappointed because they knew there'd be another one along in twenty minutes.

I believe that the Travelling Circus was also popular with the performers. Most of them stayed with my great-grandfather for many years. Occasionally one of the high-wire acts complained if the Big Top went over a hump-backed bridge during their performance but other than that it seems to have been a happy experience for all concerned.

My grandfather, Robert Merton, took over the business in 1857 and like his father he proved to be a shrewd entrepreneur. In 1861 he introduced the double-decker Big Top, which meant that members of the public could sit right next to the trapeze artists on specially constructed platforms. In those far off devil-may-care days people were often encouraged to join in. And it was common to see old men and women terrified out of their skins swinging back and forth over a hundred-foot drop, screaming at the top of their voices. In these so called "modern times" the social services wouldn't allow it but in those days audience-participation trapeze was considered first-class family entertainment.

I suppose the whole enterprise might have thrived for ever if some damn fool hadn't started producing motor cars in the 1890s. Once people realised that they could get around independently without the ever-present smell of elephants they quickly abandoned Merton's Travelling Circus and the empire folded. This was bad news for my father who had been born in 1892 and under normal circumstances would have been expected to inherit the business. Grandfather was a broken man and spent his last few years, whenever possible, attacking motor cars with a wooden mallet.

My father Bert, a man who had sawdust in his blood, grew up in the shadow of the travelling circus. He listened to the old stories with the inevitable knowledge that those days had gone for ever. He attended an ordinary school and when he was fourteen he became an apprentice mitten maker. Not many people remember mittens these days, but at the turn of the century they were known as the poor man's glove. He endured this nightmare for eight years until the outbreak of the First World War in 1914. He attempted to enlist but was turned down on the medical grounds that he had sawdust in his blood. I believe that this massive disappointment represented a turning point in my father's life. He came to realise that he should be doing something important with his time and there was very little future in mittens so he decided to give showbiz a go.

The Music Halls were still flourishing at that time and there were plenty of opportunities for my father to break into the business. Bert never talked about the first ten years of his career and so I can only imagine they must have been very hard work with very little reward. He first met my mother Mary in 1926. By this time Bert Merton was a fairly successful variety act, specialising in skills that many jealous rivals considered pointless. He would stir water in a large glass bucket at three distinctly different speeds and sometimes anti-clockwise if the act was going down particularly well. Among his other distinctive achievements was the ability to hypnotise cigarettes, the uncanny knack of speaking Turkish in a high voice and the unrivalled capacity to force horsemeat into a jam jar. In short he was a consummate artiste. Notice that I use the word "artiste" rather than the far more common "artist", which to my ears always sounds like artiste, without the e. Judy Garland was an artiste and Picasso was an artist; that is the distinction. An artiste illuminates every performance with a transcendental brilliance while an artist can't even paint somebody's face without having a blue triangle sticking out of their ear-hole.

My mother, Mary, worked at London's Kingston Empire as a Cough Check Girl. In those days patrons were encouraged to hand their coughs in before every performance, thereby eliminating the possibility of ruining the show with a burst of uncontrollable hacking. My mother would sit in her little booth handing out cloakroom tickets in exchange for coughs and at the end of the perfor-

THE AMAZING
BERT MERTON
WILL DEMONSTRATE HIS
INCREDIBLE SKILLS (INCLUDING
HIS WORLD-RENOWNED
HYPNOTISING OF CIGARETTES) ON
WEDNESDAY 12TH JULY AT THE
SOUTHPORT APOLLO.
TICKETS AVAILABLE AT THE DOOR
DOORS OPEN AT 7.00PM
COME EARLY TO AVOID DISAPPOINTMENT

mance, provided you could produce the appropriate ticket, you were reunited with your cough which I have to say was more or less unaltered by the experience. Some unscrupulous customers would try to offload their "lung-rumblers" as we called them in those days by sneaking out of a side door before the end of the evening but generally speaking people played the game by the rules. This was Mary's first job in the theatre and like many young girls she was attracted by the bright lights and the cosy glamour of the showbiz world. She was formally educated until the age of eleven when somebody stole the school textbook. Throughout her teenage years she looked after her elderly mother and when the old lady eventually passed away she applied for the job of Cough Check Girl at the Kingston Empire.

My father had played this venue on three separate occasions before 1926 and the local audiences were very appreciative of his efforts. Even if they physically attacked him after the show they would avoid punching him in the face because it was considered bad form to leave visible marks.

On 26th August 1926 at 9.17 in the evening my father leapt off the stage to the enthusiastic booing and collected his props together before popping outside the stage door for a quick breath of tobacco. He struck up conversation with the stage doorman and soon the talk got around to matters of the heart.

"What do you reckon to women these days?" asked the doorman.

"Women these days?" replied my father. "Same as they ever was, I reckon."

"No, they've changed," argued the doorman.

"A few years back you could have any woman you wanted for a bag of toffees and that included Queen Victoria. Nowadays they don't want to know. You might just as well spoonfeed them horse muck. Mind, I reckon that new Cough Check Girl has taken a shine to you."

"Mary?" said my father. "She's a pretty girl, fair enough."

"Harry Houdini's doing a special midnight show at the Chiswick Empire tomorrow night. Why don't you take her?"

"Harry Houdini!" replied father. "But I'd heard he cancelled."

"No, he couldn't get out of his contract. Take her, she'd enjoy it. She gets lonely stuck in that little booth of hers."

And so my father did. Mary enjoyed the show immensely and I think Bert did too although he did feel the odd twinge of professional jealousy watching Houdini's performance that night. His act consisted of a member of the audience tying him into a straitjacket before placing a bowler hat stuffed with explosives on to his head. The audience member then lit a fuse before retiring to his seat in the stalls. But something went wrong that night and Houdini's head exploded into thousands of pieces before he'd had time to escape from the strait-jacket. It was a spectacular sight and the audience applauded with great enthusiasm. Although to a trained eye Houdini was clearly seriously injured he nevertheless acknowledged the applause with a cheery wave. My father always claimed that it was this accident that led to Houdini's premature death some months later. My mother and father discussed the relative merits of the show as they walked home through the moonlit street.

"He's rubbish."

"Oh I don't think so, Bert. He's a great showman – you have to give him that. Of course, he hasn't got your range."

"Do you mean that, Mary?" my father said suddenly stopping and really looking properly at my mother for the first time. She was more than pretty. The moonlight

Houdini's unfortunate accident at the Chiswick Empire was captured here by early cameras with unbelievable clarity.

sparkled in her eyes and he kissed her gently on the fore-head. At that first touch Mary knew that this was the man she wanted to spend the rest of her life with. And Bert felt the same. Not that I mean that he felt he was the man he wanted to spend the rest of his life with; although obviously he would do that. Whenever he shaved first thing in the morning he'd be right there looking back at himself in the bathroom mirror. There wasn't a thing he could do about it. Nor would he want to and I think he was wise in that respect. I certainly wouldn't want to look at my reflection and see Arthur Conan Doyle looking back at me thank you very much. No, we are who we are.

As I sit here in my luxurious Spanish villa just a stone's throw from the sea composing these words, it strikes me that "we are who we are" is a pretty good definition of life. After all everybody is just one person. Apart I suppose from these people we hear of in America who have sixteen distinctly different personalities but they're all nutcases, so why should we take any notice of them? But enough true insight into the human condition, let's get back to the interesting stuff – my life story.

Bert and Mary were in love and they contrived to meet as often as possible. However, this wasn't easy as my father's act took him all over the country. So after several prolonged absences my mother resigned her job as a cough check girl and joined my father on the road where he was waiting for her just outside the theatre. The two of them surprised a lot of people by marrying very quickly, the ceremony lasted only eleven seconds, and they made the fateful decision to form a double act. It made a lot of sense for the two of them to work together and although my mother had no performing experience my father put this down to the simple fact that she had never done it before. They settled on a name, The Marvelettes, and spent several weeks devising a new act. Their early efforts weren't particularly successful. Clearly inspired by Houdini, The Marvelettes claimed they could escape from time itself. They'd take the stage with an alarm clock and a straitjacket. Mother would tie father into the jacket while pointing out to the audience that the clock was set at 2.15. They would then remain motionless until mother remarked that the clock now showed 2.20. Father would then claim that although he had not escaped from the jacket he had certainly escaped from time because it was no longer 2.15. The public didn't really go for this much even though my parents encouraged them to "ooh" and "ahh" as the seconds ticked away. Mother and father ran the act for a couple of weeks until an irate theatre manager collared them backstage in Aberdeen and curtly informed them both that, in his opinion, not only had they failed to escape time but they'd be hard pressed to escape Aberdeen.

These were dark days for my parents. For the next three and a half years they struggled. Not only was the act wrong but they were also represented by Billy Castell, known to all as possibly the shyest theatrical agent ever to work in showbusiness. Rumour had it that he owned several small offices round the back of Tottenham Court Road. But this could never be proved because no one knew anybody who had ever been there. None of his acts knew what he looked like because none of them had ever met him, and nobody knew his phone number either. His usual method of communication was to leave envelopes at the stage door for the acts he represented. These envelopes contained details of the following week's engagement and a cheque covering any outstanding money owing. And because Billy only charged five per cent commission, much lower than any other agent, his clients were happy to indulge his eccentric behaviour. Sometimes he employed even more bizarre methods of communication.

One popular act in those days, Harry Bishop And His Syncopated Neck Muscles, was playing the Friday matinée at the Brixton Empire when his act was interrupted by a rather drunken heckler: "Why don't you go to Bradford Alhambra next Monday?" shouted the heckler in a broad Glaswegian accent. By all accounts Harry was completely startled. He was not the sort of act that attracted much heckling and for a second he stumbled. For a terrible moment his neck muscles stopped syncopating just as he was about to tackle the third and final chorus of "Alexander's Ragtime Band". Before Harry could think of a response the heckler continued, "Why don't you catch the train Sunday afternoon and stay at your usual digs because a room has already been booked for you so you might as well."

As the cold sweat ran down his back Harry suddenly twigged that this drunk might actually be his agent Billy Castell. He signalled into the wings and one of the stagehands ran around the back of the theatre and into the upper circle to try to pinpoint the heckler. He found a loudspeaker propped up in a seat. He followed the wire attached to the speaker and traced it back down the stairs through the main foyer, out of the theatre and into a side alleyway. By now other people had joined the chase. In the alleyway they found a small amplifier, a ribbon microphone and a rather dog-eared copy of a book entitled *Correct Glaswegian Pronunciation*. But no sign of the heckler. The following Sunday Harry caught the train to Bradford, found his usual digs had been booked for him and on Monday he started a week's engagement at the Alhambra. The rest of the week ran smoothly for him apart from the second show Thursday when a voice from the upper circle suddenly shouted out in a broad Somerset accent, "I'm not Glaswegian any more."

Although my parents weren't working much at this time they had cause for celebration when yours truly was born on 25th October 1930. I certainly wasn't planned. Mother and Father had got drunk one night on cheap cooking oil and nine months later there I was. I think Mother may have wanted other children after me but I would never let her. I made my feelings very clear at a relatively early age. I've always thought that one child is more than enough for parents to lavish all the love and attention in the world on, and having brothers and sisters would simply dilute the effectiveness of such affection. At birth I weighed seven pounds seven ounces and according to my mother I had the bluest eyes that anybody had ever seen. I've always been proud of my eyes and throughout my professional career I've worked hard to maintain their beautiful clearness. Bright eyes are very important in television –

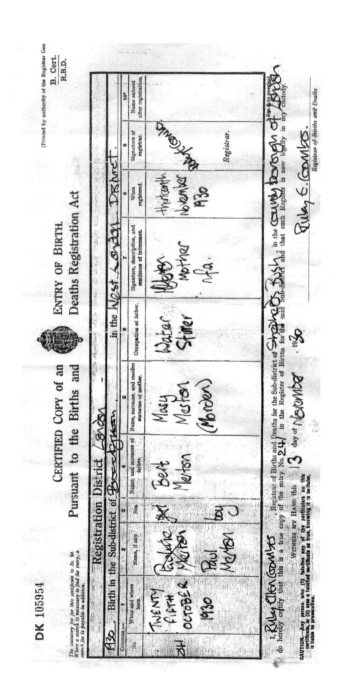

Music Hall + Baby = £££

Ideas

Baby Juggling? 
(no good —
only one baby)

Trapeze 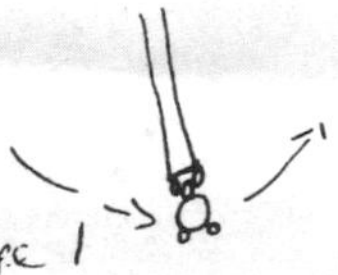
Nope!

Impressions?
how many famous
babies are there?

Magic act?
— Don't know any
baby tricks,
+ too small to
saw in half

Lion taming
just plain daft!

Mind reading
hmmm... possible

Stand up routine
Does Paul know any good jokes?
— in fact, he can't even speak!

mime act
Sounds good

Go for
this
one.

Firing from canon 
Sounds a bit
complicated

they allow you to look straight into the camera and establish proper control over the people at home. With the right technique you can *make* the viewers love you. And I mean really *love* you. If you get it right they would no more think of switching you off than they would consider sticking their firstborn into a microwave. I know some might regard this as rather cynical, but so what if people only love me because I make them? Isn't that what babies do instinctively, for God's sake?

With a newborn child and no work prospects my parents were at a low ebb. From my father's meagre savings they had managed to find the deposit for an artist's impression of a third-floor flat in Victoria, but clearly work had to be found. It was my mother Mary who hit on the idea of building a new act around the three of us. Although I was only three months old at the time, my mother saw great possibilities for the future. My father didn't take too much convincing and together the two of them began to jot ideas down on paper. Because I hadn't yet developed any real personality of my own, my parents decided that I should become a mime artist. All I had to do was to make stupid faces and incomprehensible arm movements while Mum and Dad attempted to translate this behaviour into a mild satire on the government of the day. On the occasions when I suddenly burst into

Established 1879 No 1342 22 January 1931

1d

Chelsea Ch

Smoke Gibralters
"they cure the common cold"

Fighting for Justice for All

Stage

It was with some trepidation that I attended the recent performance by the Marvelettes at the Chelsea Roxy. My instincts were correct. It can be safely said that it was the most horrendous night I have endured in all my years of review-ing for this venerable paper. Do not pay to see this rubbish. In fact if you do happen to meet the Marvelettes in the street, do not hesitate to accost them with the severest verbal abuse.

Radio

What utter tosh is on the wire-less the~~

Water Sho on the W

Due to the fact that drains are suspected of stealing large quan-tities of water from Britains glo-rious reservoirs, it is likely t' severe water shortar~~
the wa~~
C~

tears my father would solemnly announce to the audience: "Ladies and gentlemen, Mr Ramsay MacDonald." This joke may not mean much to a modern audience but I can assure you it meant even less in 1931.

For a while this act was considered even worse than the "escaping from time" routine. A contemporary review printed in the *Fulham Chronicle* gave a full flavour of our then current act:

"The undoubted low-light of the evening's presentation was the appearance of the Marvelettes, formerly a rather tatty double act who have taken it into their heads to inflict their newborn child on to the British public. Despite the father's proclamations I do not believe that a baby attempting to sit up is 'a miracle of nature'. Nor do I subscribe to the view that a young child kicking its legs in the air is somehow doing something that in any way could be described as 'magic'. I sincerely hope that you do not catch this act because I've got the suspicion it might be highly contagious."

Billy Castell did his best to drum up interest by printing large posters publicising the act and distributing them around the shops in whichever area we happened to be playing. These posters became the target of rather infantile

graffiti artists and years later father told me how angry he'd become one afternoon in Carlisle when he saw one of the posters defaced with thick black ink. Under the words "You won't believe what this Baby can do" somebody had scrawled "He eats boomerangs." Bert was so incensed he marched straight into the police station and demanded that every single inhabitant of Carlisle should be made to write the offending words so that their handwriting could be compared to the original defacement. That the police didn't simply ignore him is a measure of the esteem in which music-hall artistes were held in those days. They beat him to a pulp, bundled him into the back of a police car, drove him to the local greyhound track and tied both his feet to the electric hare in time for the first race of the evening. Thankfully he remained unconscious throughout the meeting and was blissfully unaware when the favourite won the 8.45 and bit him on the arse down the home stretch.

Of course Mother knew nothing of this and the two of us had to go on that night and try to make the act work without father. Fortunately for her the world suddenly discovered that I was a comic genius.

In spite of my tender months, I somehow must have sensed that this was make or break time. The orchestra played our music, we entered stage left, Mum carrying me in her arms. As the spotlight hit us I gurgled charmingly. Mother put me down on the stage. I then proceeded to crawl out of the spotlight much to the general amusement of the audience. Mother pulled me back and then if you please, I moved out of the spotlight in the other direction. This brought a huge cheer from the auditorium. To describe what happened next allow me to quote from my first biography, *Baby Paul, the Wonder of the Age.*

"Upon hearing the huge cheering, Baby Paul stopped crawling and turned his head to the front. His deadpan expression produced even more laughter from the audience. And just as the laughter subsided Baby Paul blew a brilliantly timed raspberry that brought the house down. As soon as the act was over it was clear that everyone had just witnessed one of the greatest showbusiness evenings in the history of Carlisle."

Later that night, back at the digs, as mother bathed father's bitemarks in iodine, she related the full story of our triumph. Dad much to his credit immediately realised that I had undoubtedly made myself the star of the act. He also knew that it was imperative to tell Billy Castell the good news as soon as possible.

In showbusiness one has to strike while the iron is at least bare medium temperature and Dad understood that new publicity had to be organised and that a London date should be arranged as quickly as possible. He decided that whatever his next step was, though, it could at least wait till morning.

The family slept comfortably that night. If they had known what lay just ahead of them, I've no doubt that Mother and Father would have paced the room all night.

Chapter 2

Being contacted by Billy Castell was one thing, but trying to contact *him* was an entirely different concern. Dad hadn't had occasion to do it before, but he had a good idea of the principles involved: You had to place a cryptic advertisement in the second-hand fridges section of *Dalton's Weekly*. A typical ad would read "Fridge wanted for two weeks in Birmingham. Contact Box 34." To the tutored eye this meant that one of Billy's acts was looking for two weeks engagement in Birmingham. A casual reader would probably dismiss the wording as a misprint. A reply from Billy would usually appear the following week but annoyingly for the acts concerned not necessarily under second-hand fridges. The Zambes Brothers, a terrible juggling act, thought that Billy had forgotten them until they finally found his reply placed under the outboard motor section in anagram form.

The week after my triumphant performance in Carlisle the following advert was placed in *Dalton's Weekly*. "Exciting New Fridge. Seeks London Location. Box 101." Although impatient for a reply, we knew how the system worked and we knew we had to wait a week. Except we didn't. The day after the advert appeared Dad went shopping. He liked to occasionally while away an evening by listening to dance band records on his wind-up gramophone. That night he brought home a copy of the "Lloyd George March" by Lew Stone and his Orchestra, a popular hit in its day. We had our tea and then sat back to listen to the familiar stirring sound. Mother told me many years later that in those days you'd often hear people singing the chorus in public places.

"A stronger nation we can forge
If we march just like Lloyd George."

But when Dad played his record we didn't hear Lew Stone and his Orchestra. Instead we heard this:

"Hello Bert, hello Mary and hello Baby Paul. Congratulations on Carlisle. I understand your desire to play London as soon as possible although I must advise caution at this stage. Baby Paul is certainly a comic genius but I do suggest that you work out and rehearse a new act thoroughly before presenting it at the London Palladium. I'll be in touch."

Because Dad didn't recognise the voice he knew instantly that it belonged to Billy Castell. Mum and Dad took a deep breath. The London Palladium! To play the Palladium was normally considered the height of any performer's career and to have the possibility placed in

Established 1880   No 1256   12 March 1931

Carlisle Ch

In Tune With the Masses

1d

A Star is Born!

Last night our historic town saw another landmark in its glorious history, for last night at the Majestic a new act hit the stage and a star was born.

Rarely in the life of this organ have we featured a theatrical review on the front page. But this is not merely a review, this is news.

The act – Baby Paul and His Associates. The night – electrifying. Baby Paul is but a few months old. But in his eyes even the untutored eye can see the experience of generations – comic perf⌐⌐

It was then, with great surprise, theat "The Associates" are in fact an obscure music hall act that I had had the misfortune to see before when they were the abysmal "Marvelettes". It would be an understatement to say that this act was responsible for the worst night of my life and precipitated the break up of marriage. But now
PAI⌐⌐

has the most amazing sense of comic timing that I have ever seen. You won't believe ⌐ you see it for yourself ⌐
that y⌐⌐ ⌐
I⌐

front of them literally took their breath away. Naturally they took a deep breath before their breath was taken away because it wouldn't have worked the other way round. My parents weren't stupid.

The next day the rehearsals began. Because of my very tender age and the likelihood that I would probably mess up large chunks of difficult dialogue it was decided that the new act should be entirely visual. My parents eventually settled on the idea of shooting me out of a cannon centre-stage and straight into the Royal Box where King George V would catch me in his arms, hold me aloft and declare to the audience, "It is our patriotic duty to support and cherish this brilliant young entertainer."

We rehearsed for several weeks in a disused warehouse in Bermondsey. My father carefully recreated the dimensions of the Palladium stage with a large net suspended from the roof which in a rather uncanny manner completely failed to simulate King George V sitting in the Royal Box. Once the trajectory had been fully worked out to my father's satisfaction he realised that ideally, and so as to leave nothing to chance, it was imperative that we should rehearse with the King himself. Dad placed an advert in *Dalton's Weekly* and received a reply from Billy Castell via pigeon post. The upshot was that the following Monday morning King George was to be found sitting at the top of a tall stepladder in a disused warehouse in Bermondsey attempting to catch a five-month-old baby

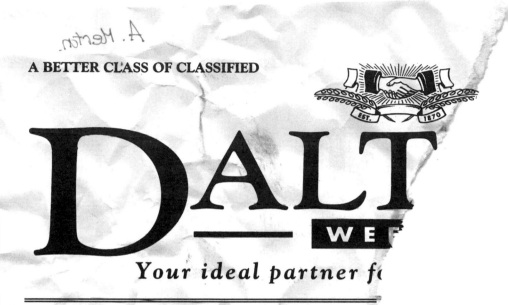

A. Merton.

A BETTER CLASS OF CLASSIFIED

DALT

WEE

Your ideal partner f

SECOND-HAND FRIDGES

KITCHEN

- **Fridge**, fair condition, Box.132
- **Fridge** with ice box, fits under worktop, can deliver, Box.201
- **Fridge** in good condition, Box.84
- **Exciting new fridge** seeks London location, Box.101
- **Upright fridge**, works, Box.62
- **Fridge**, excellent condition, first to see will buy, Box.99
- **Larder fridge**, all fixtures as new, Box.213
- **Electrolux fridge**, white, with ice box, very good working order, Box.183
- **Fridge**, with three year guarantee, Box.42

- **Fridge**, with small freezer compartment, good working condition, Box.205
- **Successful fridge**, needs something for the summer season, Box.35
- **Fridge**, white, in good condition for year, Box.162
- **Hotpoint fridge**, excellent condition, Box.189
- **Multi-talented fridge**, does perfect Winston Churchill impression, anything in Cornwall?, Box.109
- **Big fridge**, it's big, Box.56
- **Fridge**, full ser... a nice run...

- **Beautiful fitted kitch** oak, including coc Box.135
- **Belfast sink**, very condition, buyer c Box.223
- **Kitchen cabin** standing 69 x 21 shelves, Box.84
- **Kitchen tab'** Box.50

fired from a military cannon of dubious vintage. Like most keen amateurs with a deep love of showbusiness he was completely useless. On the first six hundred attempts he dropped me every time and but for the judicious placing of double thick mattresses around the base of the stepladder the career of Baby Paul would surely have reached an abrupt conclusion.

Mother also took the precaution of fitting me with a super rubberised nappy which allowed me to bounce quite happily up and down for some time without suffering any hardship. Trying to catch a bouncing baby is not always so easy and if it looked like I would continue bouncing for quite some time my parents and the King would retire to a nearby snack bar for double egg and chips before returning some while later to find a rather dizzy but contented baby gurgling away to its heart's content.

At last my father decided that the act was ready which was a great relief to the King who had kindly cancelled a visit from the King of Sweden on the grounds that he, George, the ruler over Great Britain's vast Empire and Dominions, was too busy rehearsing a music-hall act to meet him at the railway station. This did not go down particularly well with the King of Sweden who rudely informed Buckingham Palace that the next time George V

"Knobbly-knees."

called on him, he would not find him at home but instead judging a knobbly-knees contest just outside Stockholm.

Diplomats smoothed the situation over and we got excited about our opening night. On 15th April 1931 we presented our act to the great British public at the London Palladium. Now billed simply as Baby Paul and Associates we followed a well-known double act of the day called Moony and Sad who specialised in dying on their feet or at least they did every time I worked with them. People who understand showbusiness will know what I mean when I describe Moony and Sad as having a juggler's sense of comedy – i.e. none. The first account of what happened that night at the London Palladium was published in the London *Times* two days later.

"The undoubted highlight of the show was the London début of a remarkable act called Baby Paul and his Associates. Although short it was spectacular in its theatricality. It began with Baby Paul's parents placing him inside a cannon and then firing him towards the Royal Box to the sound of a large explosion and frightened gasps from the audience who feared for the life of our gracious sovereign. However, the King silenced the gasps by grabbing the baby out of thin air and immediately dropping it into the orchestra pit. The whole action was so smooth that if your correspondent hadn't known better he would have sworn the whole thing was carefully rehearsed. Upon reaching the orchestra pit Baby Paul contrived to bounce off the heads of several musicians in a manner not unlike a flat stone skimming off the the surface of a mill pond. Upon hitting a timpani drum Baby Paul was catapulted back up towards the stage. And then with a remarkable piece of timing an unknown hand threw a tennis racket on to the stage which Baby Paul's father grabbed just as his son was dropping towards him. With a beautifully executed overhead smash, that would have graced any Wimbledon finals, Baby Paul was once again propelled towards the Royal Box where this time His Majesty grabbed the child, held him above his head and told the audience in a beautifully clear tone tinged perhaps with no small measure of excitement, 'Well I buggered that up, didn't I?' The King's subjects roared with laughter at this extraordinarily funny remark and it was some minutes before order could be restored. When it was clear that His Majesty was to continue his address a hushed tone spread around the theatre. 'It is our patriotic duty,' he said, 'to support and cherish this brilliant young entertainer.' The resultant cheers I am reliably informed could be heard as far away as Leicester Square."

And so with Royal endorsements my fantastic show-business career was off to a flying start. Afterwards, we were all still heady with excitement when our celebrations were interrupted by a knock at the dressing-room door. Father opened the door and for the first time in his life he set eyes on Warner Toland, the then famous independent American film producer. Mr Toland loved what

An emotional night for all at the London Palladium, 15th April 1931
mere moments before King George V uttered his immortal lines.

Established 1881   No 1205   14 July 1931

London Ch

Just In It For A Laugh

1d

Smoke
Gibralters
*"they're
make you
beautiful"*

Baby Paul is London Palladium Sensation

The show at the Palladium is always a joy. It is the best venue in the best city in the world. However the show two days ago was the best yet.

The performances by all concerned were outstanding. But the undoubted highlight of the show was the London debut of a remarkable act called Baby Paul and his Associates. Although show is lar...

remarkable piece of timing an unknown hand threw a tennis racket on to the stage with Baby Paul's father grabbed just as his son was dropping towards him. With a beautifully execu... overhead smash, th... have g...

T

he saw and with the patriotic cries still ringing in our ears Dad signed a five-year contract for yours truly to appear in a series of Hollywood motion pictures.

At ten months old I was on the threshold of becoming the biggest star in the world. With all the excitement of the occasion nobody thought to wonder who it was who had thrown the tennis racket to my father from the side of the stage. The move had never even been thought of let alone rehearsed. But whoever had done it had provided me with a barnstorming finish. Looking back on it now as I sit in my luxurious Spanish villa, I have little real doubt that it was Billy Castell. Who but he would have had the presence of mind to bring a tennis racket to the London Palladium on the off chance that it would be needed in an emergency? And who persuaded His Majesty King George V to rehearse with an unknown variety act for two months with no question of a fee? Exactly how much influence did our secretive agent have? For the moment these questions must remain unanswered.

It's a beautiful day today. The sun is high in the sky and I'm relaxing by the pool of my luxurious Spanish villa. It's been a quiet morning. It's the maid's day off and my wife is away visiting her sister in Argentina. Although by right she should have returned a couple of hours ago, I'm far from concerned. She is a dear but she has no sense of time, poor thing. She'll turn up some time this afternoon or early evening blissfully unaware that she is late or that I've been stuck here on my own in my luxurious Spanish villa all day. I am of retirement age, for God's sake, and although I'm perfectly capable of looking after myself, a little consideration wouldn't go entirely amiss. I may have words when she returns, depending on the lateness of the hour.

The family arrived in Hollywood just before Christmas 1931. In those days travelling to America meant enduring a six-week voyage on a passenger ship in the company of people who had no connection with showbusiness. Our living quarters were so cramped that Mother had to stand on Father's shoulders. But soon they got used to it and for

Pan-Atlantic

5328/A5

Passage to the Americas on: 2nd November 1930, 4.00pm

For: Mr & Mrs A Merton + child

Your ship: Pride of Hartlepool

Accommodation: Single cabin on L deck, full economy board

All at Pan-Atlantic wish you a pleasant voyage

See reverse for full conditions of transit

several years afterwards Mother would jump up on Dad's shoulders whenever they were feeling nostalgic. The food served up by the ship's crew consisted of very salty water and nothing else. I've no idea where they got it from but there certainly seemed to be a lot of it. The other passengers, as I've mentioned, were ordinary members of the public and I think Dad tried talking to one of them once but it's very difficult to maintain a conversation with somebody whose life is far less interesting than your own. It's certainly been true in my experience. I suppose as an artiste I'm blessed with imagination and a sensitivity that sets me apart from the majority of people who make up nine-tenths of the planet.

Upon arriving in the USA we were greeted by a headline in *Variety*, the American showbiz bible: "Limey Baby Puts Tinseltown Brats to the Test". The article underneath pushed the rather unfortunate angle that somehow I had arrived in Hollywood to poach American film parts from American babies and that I was hell bent on building a film career and didn't care who I crawled over to achieve it. It was unfortunate because although none of the family had spoken to the press – I was only twelve months old and still naive in the ways of language – the reporter through sheer luck had correctly guessed my father's strategy. Because I still couldn't talk, Dad reckoned that by the time I had learnt to speak it would be with an American accent and everyone would assume I was Yankee born and bred. In that case I wouldn't then be handed a lot of unsatisfying supporting roles playing an English baby on a visit to his American cousins.

Our first Christmas in America was a miserable affair. Although Warner Toland had booked the family into a wonderful suite at the Regency Hotel, nobody in Hollywood knew who I was. Mother carried me in her arms up and down Hollywood Boulevard but no crowds gathered around me. To be considered a nobody at twelve months old was a thoroughly humiliating experience and I wouldn't recommend it to anyone.

Once the so-called Christmas celebrations were out of the way it was time to get to work. The first film I made was a western called *Cattle Queen of Montana*. I played a character called Bucky Junior. Although still too young for dialogue I managed to make some impression and garnered generally good reviews for the scene where I threw my rattle at a Sioux Indian. The next film was a gangster picture called *Bootleg Liquor*. Again no dialogue but some critics praised the rather comical expression on my face when James Cagny gunned down seventeen hoodlums crammed inside a shower cubicle.

For the next six months the pattern continued. I made musicals, war films, historical dramas, biblical epics and in each and every one I played a character called Bucky Junior. Clearly my career was in a rut. Not being able to speak was a handicap. Fine for silent films but audiences in the early thirties demanded dialogue. Mum and Dad realised they had to get me talking as soon as possible. To that end they talked at me non-stop for twenty-four hours a day, each of them taking a twelve-hour shift. It was exhausting for us all but the work paid off and after several weeks I'd managed to acquire a vocabulary of 15,000 words. Now that I was able to express myself fully, the family sat down and worked out our next move. Although I had appeared in over a dozen movies, in each and every one I had been typecast as a baby. We had to convince Warner Toland that I was capable of a far greater range.

We met in his office. Warner hadn't seen me for a month, so he was somewhat amazed when I talked to him directly.

"Listen, Warner," I said. "So far I've played cameos and that's fine. I'm new to the town and I understand the necessity of building slowly. But in all honesty this baby stuff is restricting. Now I may be only nineteen months old but think of the novelty value of casting me in adult roles. It's never been done before."

VARIETY

Limey Baby Puts Tinseltown Brats to the Test

Would you believe it, those limey Brits have sent over a baby brat to steal all the plum jobs from our all-American babies.

Yesterday morning Universal Arthritis' latest aquistion turned up in Hollywood via train and express boat from the UK. By lunchtime 'Bob' (the bouncing baby) had been dropped from the forthcoming Castle Queen of Montana project in favor of 'Baby Paul'. No doubt within a coupl

Now color me red, go up and down in an elavator, put your foot down on the gas (minding the fender of the automobile in front) and dance around on the sidewalk, but an English baby in a Western? What is the world coming to?

Those Brits don't know anything about mom's apple pie or what made the good ol US of A the great place it is today.

He looked thoughtful for a moment and toyed with a silver cigarette box on his desk. As he lifted the lid a glint of sunlight dazzled my eyes and I immediately burst into tears. I cried like a baby for several minutes, which in my view was perfectly understandable, although everybody else in the office was clearly distressed. Once I'd regained my composure I explained that although I was perfectly fluent I was still prone to lapsing into normal baby behaviour if something unexpected happened. Warner understood.

"Listen," he said, "it's a miracle you talking anyway. And I think you're right. I've got a couple of screenplays I'd like you to take a look at."

"That's great," said Mum. "But remember Baby Paul can't read yet. That will take a while longer. We'll read the scripts to him and if he likes them we'll be in touch."

While everybody else shook hands I attempted to stroll about but had to give up after falling down several times. It had been a good meeting but if anyone of us had seriously thought about exactly what had just happened we would have been a lot less confident about the future.

The first major motion picture I starred in was called *Baby Paul Meets the Man of Mars*. I wasn't entirely happy with the picture even when we were making it. Although I was playing the commander of a spaceship my role chiefly consisted of sitting in a high chair with a goldfish bowl over my head. The dialogue was fairly wooden as well. There's only so much feeling you can put into a speech that begins with the line "Routine soil analysis indicates an atmosphere of thirty-four per cent oxygen." Although I was far from pleased with my own performance the general public loved every second of it. The intrinsic novelty of seeing a baby crawling across an alien landscape while battling against zero gravity and colic had them queuing right around the block. It was the biggest money-making picture of 1931. People in the industry were beginning to take notice of me.

My next picture broke all previous box-office records and is still shown regularly on television today, in the late-night movie slots. I of course refer to the most famous film to emerge from that early talkies period: *Bedwetters of 1932*. Audiences were astounded that a two-year-old baby could handle fast wise-cracking dialogue and carry a tune as well. Understandably the stand-out scene in *Bedwetters* as I like to call it was my rendition of the song "Wake Me Up Before I Go Go". This quickly became the biggest selling song of these Depression years and at one time it seemed that everybody owned a copy of it. Christmas 1932 was a joy compared to Christmas 1931. We threw a huge party in our newly purchased Beverley

This is the only surviving photograph of independant Hollywood producer Warner Toland (second left). Amusingly you will notice his bandaged right hand – a result of a nasty nip from Your's Truly.

Hills mansion. The guest list was a *Who's Who* of Hollywood. Everybody wanted to meet me.

We started work on my next film *Baby Paul Tapdances to Rio* at the beginning of 1933. It was a fairly routine version of a familiar story. A single mother needs money for a special operation so her baby son undertakes a sponsored tap dance across Brazil to raise the necessary funds. We've all seen it filmed a thousand times before. The only unique aspect of our version was that for the first time I had to play a character actually older than myself. I was cast as a five-year-old. This proved to be a big mistake. Although I could talk perfectly well and my walking was improving every day, emotionally I was still only two years old. Because I was so articulate people forgot this. Three days into shooting I threw my first tantrum. I took a severe dislike to the lighting cameraman. Every time I saw his stupid face I threw a cup of warm milk at him. Being a big star everybody on the set pretended it wasn't happening, including the lighting cameraman. As soon as one cup of warm milk had been thrown, another was placed in my hands. Once I had thrown that it was replaced by another and so on. For three continuous days I chucked endless cups of milk over this unfortunate character. If the studio had disciplined me at this point by imposing heavy fines or sending me to bed early I might have behaved myself but they didn't. Soon I got tired of this particular game and decided to say no to everything. Could I do this? Could I do that? No no no! Warner Toland was called to the studio floor. I ignored him. My mother and father were summoned. Nobody could persuade me to work. Two more days were wasted in this fashion. The following Monday, already a week behind schedule, we attempted a fresh start. Suddenly I was co-operative. We made great headway for the next few days and everybody told me I was marvellous, as indeed I was. Now, I can't say that my improved behaviour was a conscious decision on my part. As much as I wanted to stick out my lower lip or laugh at nothing in particular I found it impossible. Mum and Dad of course noticed the change but put it down to an innate sense of profession-alism. Only Warner Toland knew the truth.

I was being drugged. Every morning before shooting began Warner gave me a square of chocolate liberally coated with a substance called Desquioquin. If taken on a daily basis it induces a highly suggestive state. In other words if I was told what to do I would do it. The director Hugo Washtansky, a foreign emigré who had left Poland in a hurry when he realised that nobody there liked him very much, managed to draw the most extraordinary performance from me. If he wanted wistful I gave him wistful. Everybody was ecstatic about the work I was putting in. After three weeks' filming we were back on schedule. By the end of that week I had completed all my close-ups and reaction shots. We had five days left. Five days in which to film a fairly lengthy sequence of Baby Paul tapdancing across Brazil. Monday morning disaster struck. I couldn't tapdance to save my life. Despite my best efforts I simply didn't have the proper muscular

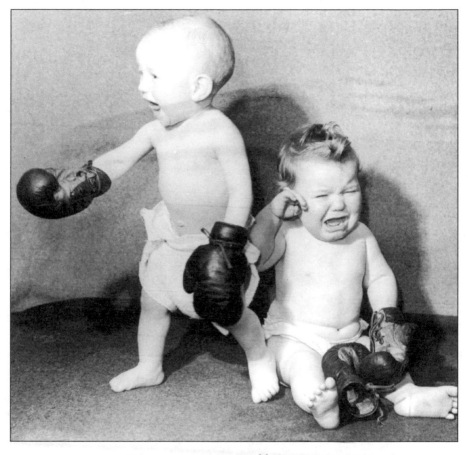

*Whenever possible I would give the other
on-set babies a right bashing.*

development. That's when Warner Toland put me on steroids. Within two days I had legs like an orang-utan. On the Thursday I was so eager to please that I tapdanced continuously for seventeen hours and only stopped when a tranquilliser dart was fired into the back of my neck.

Filming was completed and *Baby Paul Tapdances to Rio* became my third big hit in a row. But once the film was over the drug Desquioquin continued to play a large part in my life. Because it placed me in a highly suggestive state I was prone to all sorts of strange behaviour depending on whatever odd phrases I picked up in conversation around me. If somebody said "Go to hell" I would attempt to tunnel down through the carpet and invoke the spirit of Beelzebub. Luckily, being such a young child, my infantile efforts to summon up the Prince of Darkness never really got any further than conjuring up the odd whiff of sulphur. But there was no question that I was now the greatest star in the world. I was also a drug addict fast getting out of control.

Chapter 3

Throughout 1932, 1933 and 1934 I made seventeen films, all of them box office smashes. No matter what kind of film I made, the public loved it. Perhaps my most bizarre film in this period was called *Baby Paul Kisses a Salmon*. To quote from the publicity: "A simple touching story of a baby's love for a fish". I didn't enjoy making the film very much. Fish are very difficult to work with. They have limited facial expressions and because they can't remember anything for more than ten seconds it's impossible for them to maintain a consistent characterisation. One minute the fish would be all coquettish and the next we'd be getting some tough guy performance that was totally out of keeping with the tone of the picture. I vowed never to work with animals again and I knew my career would have to be in a very bad shape before I would even consider it. The fish seemed to enjoy the experience, however, and later changed its name to Edward G. Robinson and of course the rest is history.

As far as the outside world was concerned I was adorable and could do no wrong. I only wish I had been around to enjoy it. By this time I was pumped full of so many different drugs they were coming out of my ears. As an example, for the title role in *Young Abraham Lincoln*, I

An early portrait of the fish now known to all as Edward G. Robinson.

was given male hormones so I could grow my own beard. Of course Mum and Dad noticed that I'd become increasingly volatile. I was obnoxious, demanding, superior, two-faced, spiteful, and manipulative to such an extent I was no different from any other star in Hollywood. My parents assumed this was par for the course. My metabolism was so screwed up that my body ballooned and shrank all the time. I know other people have suffered with this but in my case you could see it happening. In any given fifteen-minute time span my weight would fluctuate between two and a half stone and eleven stone. This was difficult to deal with. In a half-hour business meeting I was either trying to stop my trousers falling down or attempting to prevent my jacket splitting up the back and my shirt buttons flying off at all angles. It soon became impossible to make a film.

After four days spent attempting to film a musical set in the Sahara desert, and rather improbably called *Dune Tune*, work was postponed indefinitely. The problem was that none of the shots matched. I'd take a sip of coffee in close-up and then put the cup back on to the table in another shot, clearly weighing five stone heavier than I was three seconds earlier. Perhaps my career could have survived this but in that same year, 1934, America discovered Shirley Temple and I was thrown on to the

Hollywood scrapheap. I of course held Shirley Temple completely responsible for my downfall and as is well documented I took great pleasure in pulling her hair and making her cry during the 1934 Oscar ceremonies.

And so my world fell apart. I seriously contemplated ending it all but my parents as always were there to support me. I can remember my mother saying, "Never commit suicide on an empty stomach because you never know where your next meal is coming from." Nobody wanted to know us any more. Douglas Fairbanks, whom I'd come to regard as a friend, cut me dead in the supermarket one afternoon and I realised there and then it was time to go home.

We arrived back in Southampton just before Christmas 1934. We caught the train to London and attempted to avoid the press at Waterloo Station by travelling incognito. When we arrived at Waterloo despite exhaustive efforts on my part we discovered there was no press to avoid. Nobody cared tuppence. That Christmas was bleak. The family shared a single room in Kilburn. For those of you who don't know Kilburn, it's in Kilburn, in North London (see plate section). In those days it was very seedy and run down. I haven't been back there for years. God knows what it's like now. Our landlady's name was Irene. We never learnt her surname because as she said

With love from Shirley Temple

"everybody calls me Irene". She was a very stupid woman who liked to keep a huge distance between herself and personal hygiene. I'm not sure my descriptive powers are up to it but if I suggest that she smelt like she'd been dragged through several hundred yards of rhino dung and then hosed down with buffalo wee at regular intervals, you might be able to conjure up some reasonably accurate picture of her. In her tiny back garden was a dead horse buried under half a ton of housebricks. We didn't know it was there for several months until we had a hot spell and its stinking presence suddenly made itself very apparent. Irene wasn't at all bothered by this. On the contrary she greeted our complaint with a generous smile and declared that summer must be on the way.

The reason we were living in these conditions was that all the money I had earned in Hollywood had to be paid back because I had broken the "Don't Get Fat" clause in my contract. We were penniless. You don't forget bitterness like that. I suppose at the very heart of it I don't bear Shirley Temple any particular grudge, she's a lovely person, but even to this day I can't hear "On the Good Ship Lollipop" without tasting vomit at the back of my throat. The only positive aspect of leaving Hollywood was that with no regular supply of drugs my weight soon stabilised.

Shortly after Christmas Dad placed an advert in the second-hand fridges section of Dalton's Weekly. "Highly successful fridge just back from Hollywood. Needs to be converted to UK voltage". Although it had been four years since we had last communicated with him, Billy Castell replied the following week. We were sitting at home listening to Major Bermont's Syncopated Seven on the wireless when an unfamiliar voice interrupted the programme. "Hello, everybody. It's nice to have you back. I trust you are enjoying our concert of selected funeral marches from Walthamstow Library and we shall be rejoining the music in just a moment. As I speak to you I am reminded of the Chinese proverb which I seem to have forgotten for the moment. The gist however runs along the lines of the past is now gone and the future lies ahead of you. Bearing in mind your recent traumas overseas I strongly advise immediate retirement. You shall of course return and be renewed but first you must experience more of life's great treasures. Goodbye for now and for quite some time. I shall now pass you back to Major Bermont and his charming rendition of Purcell's March for Woodwind and Balustrade."

We realised immediately that it was Billy Castell and wondered how he had managed to communicate with us in such a direct manner. We searched the room for hidden loudspeakers but couldn't find any. The evening newspapers carried a story about the BBC announcing an immediate inquiry into how somebody had managed to jam the signals in order to deliver a rather cryptic message to thousands of listeners. My family were the only three people in the country who knew exactly what the message meant. Billy was right. Baby Paul had evolved into such a disaster the only way forward was to expunge all memory of him from the public consciousness. And so a plan was hatched. I was to spend many years growing up in obscurity. I would attend an ordinary bog standard junior school under my own name Paul Merton and nobody would make the connection with Baby Paul. In those days before video tape and television, if your name didn't appear on the big screen you were quickly forgotten. And I certainly was. Other stars came and went while I languished in total anonymity. It was an utterly humiliating experience and I wouldn't wish it on a cat.

I struggled through my school years and did my best to mix with ordinary simple folk, but it was very difficult to build any kind of rapport with any of them. I had been a major celebrity on a world-wide scale whereas their greatest achievement was a B-plus in shoe repairing or whatever stupid subject we were being taught at the time. The first school I went to at the age of seven was full of very stupid people and I can't really bring myself to recall the full horror of it all. I was expelled after telling the headmaster that he wouldn't know a close-up if it lived next door to him for twenty years.

My next school was again full of very stupid people but there was one teacher that I really liked. Her name was Mrs Matthews and she thought I was the loveliest child in the class. She lavished such love on me at the expense of all the other children that I couldn't help but warm to her after two or three years. I found out a long time later that my mother had been bribing her but, after all, isn't that what mothers are for?

So that was school, formative days for many no doubt, but to be honest once you've shaken hands with Clark Gable the isosceles triangle loses a great deal of its no doubt considerable charm.

War broke out in 1939 and I wished I could have done the same. Finally I escaped on 29th February 1944, a day I shall never forget. Although still many months short of my fourteenth birthday, the authorities finally released me from their grand scheme to turn me into exactly the same person as everybody else. Speaking personally, I relished my freedom, although the rest of Europe was still heavily involved in the Second World War. I sensed the opportunity to entertain the troops abroad. Unfortunately I volunteered to entertain the wrong side. I'd agreed to the bookings, but because of my poor education I had no idea that Munich was in Germany. Let me tell you, those concerts were very hard work. I didn't really have an act, so I simply collected together all the old jokes I could think of. In fact the act went so badly that once British intelligence discovered what I was up to I was positively encouraged to continue because of my invaluable role in sapping enemy morale. Indeed on the explicit orders of Winston Churchill I added a comic song. I reproduce the great man's memo on the following two pages.

I suppose it was just as well that the audiences never understood what I was singing about.

Looking back on it now, as I soak up the early afternoon sun on the verandah of my luxurious Spanish villa, I can understand some misguided people being highly critical of my actions. But I have nothing to apologise for. I was barely a teenager at the time and I simply wanted to be on whichever side was winning. And after all, England had treated me like a nobody since my return from Hollywood and I felt that I owed my country nothing. Although certainly no patriot, I was later told by Field-Marshal Montgomery himself that my efforts to entertain in every tawdry nightclub in Berlin had hastened the end of the war by eighteen months. So

TOP SECRET MEMO

FROM: WINSTON CHURCHILL, WAR BUNKER, SECRET LOCATION, UNDER LONDON, BLIGHTY

TO: BRITISH INTELLIGENCE, VARIOUS CLASSIFIED LOCATIONS

DEAR BRITISH INTELLIGENCE,

HOW ARE YOU? HOW'S THE WIFE AND KIDS?

THANK YOU FXR FOR THE NOTE YOU POPPED THROUGH THE DOOR THE OTHER DAY CONCERNING THE VERY BAD ENGLISH COMEDIAN WORKING IN GXRMXNY GERMANY.

I AGREE WITH YOUR CONCLUSIONS BUT TO MAXIMISE HIS IMPACT I SUGGEST WE PARACHUTE THE FOLLOWING COMIC SONG TO HIM.

SINCERELY,

Winston

WINSTON.

P.S. ARE YOU ALRIGHT FOR EGGS?

Merton's Travelling Circus. The birth place of modern entertainment and regular public transport.

Always taking their work home with them, my grandparents would hypnotise my father regularly as a boy. The result – he sired a showbiz legend!

A rare still from those early days. My father and I are seen here in Bermondsey, practising for the London Palladium Performance in 1931. At this stage George V had not yet joined us. I am pictured top left.

My Hollywood debut. Cattle Queen of Montana was very much a film of the times. These days babies are discouraged from smoking on-screen.

Our run down flat in Kilburn and our landlady, Irene. Irene was a very stupid woman who liked to keep a huge distance between herself and personal hygiene.

School days were some of the dullest days of my life.
The worst part was being surrounded by ordinary people.

A mix-up led to me entertaining the wrong troops during WWII.
One of the hardest gigs I ever did is pictured here, at Nuremberg.

My old pal, Peter Sellers, pictured here at his London digs. When asked for advice I told him to "Ditch the funny voices and comedy characters, Peter. There's no future in them."

Now you'd surely think me barmy
If I joined up with the army
I'm really not cut out as 'Soldier Paul'.
I suppose like my friend Davy
I could join the ruddy Navy
But I'd never get no blinking peace at all.
Now if I'm not a shrinking violet
But who wants to be a pilot
I really hope I never get the call.
They say that the Luftwaffe
Are a bunch of ruddy 'puffas'
So I'd never get no blinking peace at all.

To be sung in the style of 'Rule
Britannia'.

despite my best efforts I returned to England in 1945 a national hero.

Upon my arrival at Southampton I was greeted by the press and in the several interviews I gave that day, I made no mention of my previous career as Baby Paul and nobody made the connection. My parents were overjoyed to see me and were relieved that I was safe and well. I'd disappeared without their consent, simply leaving a note on the kitchen table: "Have gone to win the war". And in Mum and Dad's eyes I had done just that.

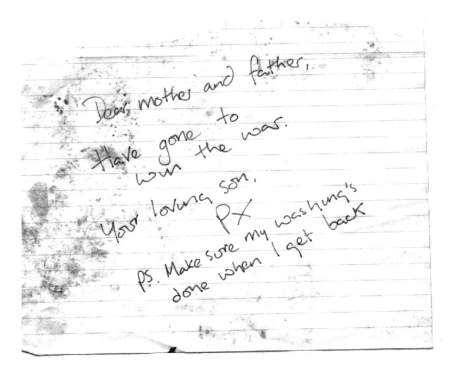

Finding immediate work after the end of hostilities was difficult. The British troops were demobilised and with them all the entertainers who had worked in concert parties. Competition was fierce. I didn't doubt my ability to compete but I had to find a new act. I was expressly banned from performing my previous act in Britain because of the devastating effect that it had on the Germans and so I sought out the advice of Billy Castell. By this time Mum and Dad had given up showbusiness. After our return from Hollywood they had attempted to revive the old water-stirring routine but Dad's wrist had gone and the act was never the same again.

By 1945 they were running a second-hand shop in the Goldhawk Road. Dad collected broken watches and providing the second hand wasn't beyond repair he would rip it out and put it into a watch that was otherwise fine apart from a broken second hand. Because Mum and Dad were so busy they gave me their blessing to pursue a solo career and so I placed my first ad in Dalton's Weekly. "For sale, top of the range fridge. Needs attention." Billy's answer took the form of a teapot thrown at my head while walking down Tottenham Court Road the following Tuesday. Shoved inside the spout was a typewritten note, "Dear Paul, I hope the delivery of this message hasn't proved to be too painful. First you have to develop an act

Dear Paul,

I hope the delivery of this message hasn't proved to be too painful. First you have to develop an act that is unique to you. Beacause you have a non-existant writing ability, I suggest you find good writers quick. Hang around some variety act and see if you can pick up any tips. I could help you but I prefer to test your commitment. I'll be in touch and I trust the bruising will soon heal up.

yours sincerely

Billy Castell

that is unique to you. Because you have a non-existent writing ability I suggest you find good writers quick. Hang around some variety acts and see if you can pick up any tips. I could help you but I prefer to test your commitment. I'll be in touch and I trust the bruising will soon heal up."

Billy's advice had always been spot-on before so I contrived to hang around the stage doors in order to strike up conversations with the artists on the bill.But it seemed that every other fifteen-year-old boy in London was hell bent on doing exactly the same thing. Sometimes I watched them from a distance. So eager to be involved, so naive, no understanding of the torture that so often walks hand in hand with the glamour. Occasionally an elderly, burnt-out variety act would send one of the boys off on a "tuppenny run". A boy would be given tuppence and told to run away as fast as possible on the under-standing that he would never return. It was a ritual left over from the old days of the music hall. And the young lads who used to hang around the stage doors were so glad to have any association with the business they would tear off in all directions, clutching their tuppences, heads held high; never once looking back.

This cleared the arena for me. I made a point of talking to the more successful acts. I saw little reason in asking the shabbier performers for advice. In many cases they had sadly let failure go to their heads. Of all the people I spoke to, Max Miller was definitely the most helpful. He was full of simple meaningful phrases – "Trousers on your head is comedy. Trousers on your legs is dignity" is one such phrase that I'll never forget. There's an old saying, "the bigger they are, the nicer they are". It was certainly true of Max and it's certainly true of me. Max put me in touch with a fifteen-year-old schoolboy called Bob Monkhouse who was selling jokes to a lot of comedians at the reasonable rate of five bob a gag. Although the material suited older comics it didn't feel right to employ somebody who was the same age as myself. I needed a newer approach. I replied to one of the many adverts placed in the back of The Stage, which is a theatrical newspaper known chiefly to the inhabitants of showbusiness as a tough, no-nonsense publication which somehow has always managed to be at the cutting edge of innovation. The ad read: "Two thousand Gags. All corkers. Yours for five and eleven." I borrowed the money off Dad but was hugely disappointed when the two thousand gags arrived and turned out to be the same rubbish I'd been peddling during the war. Although I was disappointed by Billy's lack of guidance at the time I realise now that he was giving me the chance to find my own feet. It was a year before I found regular work.

An old comic called Tony Pond eventually got tired of seeing me hanging around the back of theatres with a miserable expression on my face and took me under his wing. Although Tony had never been a big name, he had worked the halls successfully for twenty odd years or more with an entertaining schoolroom sketch. Basically, Tony played the headmaster while his two stooges acted out the parts of terminally stupid schoolboys. One of them had reached retirement age and so I was drafted in. It was the perfect part for me, having recently spent a very long time in the company of terminally stupid schoolboys. We rehearsed the act for over twenty minutes until Tony was convinced I was ready. Our first gig was the Birmingham Hippodrome. The publicity claimed that it was the first time that Paul Merton the war hero had appeared before the British public. I didn't tell a soul that many years before I had actually played the London Palladium. The first night went well as indeed did the rest of the week. Tony's act was well polished and I was happy just to be appearing in front of an audience again.

I spent the next year and a half working with Tony and they were happy days. By mid 1948 I felt it was time to move on. I've always hated saying "goodbye" so I simply didn't turn up for the show one night and never saw Tony ever again. He made several attempts to contact me but I felt it would cause less heartache all round if I refused to acknowledge his existence in any way whatsoever.

Around about this time the BBC was producing a tremendous number of light entertainment shows revolving around the armed services. These were very popular with radio audiences and no doubt some of you will remember such shows as *Raise the Flag, Battleship Ahoy* and *I Don't Want It*. This seemed a potentially rich area for me and I phoned several relevant producers but never got past any of their secretaries. Although they knew of my war efforts they also knew that my act had been, to use a showbiz term, "very bad". After several weeks of getting nowhere I attempted to enlist the help of Billy Castell. I received a reply back from him criticising the manner in which I left the schoolboy act and informing me that because he also represented Tony he took a very dim view of my unprofessional behaviour. I could ill afford upsetting Billy and I suppose I should have realised that his influence could be detrimental to my future career if he so chose. Such was his power in show-business that if word got round that Billy didn't like you everyone else assumed that behind the showbiz mask lay a personality so abnormal and twisted that any attempt to place it before the public would result in mass rioting and possibly a lynching. Such a thing actually happened to the Declan Twins, a rather poor close harmony duo who upset Billy in some way or other and attempted to book themselves on to the variety circuit. At their very first gig In Rochdale they had barely started "Don't sit under the Apple Tree with Anyone Else but Me" when an angry mob stormed the stage and tore them limb from limb. In such tragic circumstances as these my sympathies always lie with the poor unfortunate act that's got to go on next. It's never easy for any performer if the previous turn has been murdered by the audience. I once had to follow a close-up magician who was killed by a single blow to the back of the neck, and it took all my technical know-how to get the audience to return to their seats and hand in their rocks to the management.

Established 1903 No 845 12 March 1947

Rochdale C

2d

Give Us Your Money

Tragedy at the Emp

Last night was a sorry night for this town. Pictured below are the hapless Declan Twins, two young music hall performers who last night, as they say in the world of the dramatic arts, died on their feet.

Mary, 12 and Sally, 12, last night performed at the Rochdale Empire – FOR THE LAST TIME. Barely were they into their third song when hecklers, increasingly upset by the twins poor rendition of "Don't Sleep Under The Apple Tree With Any One Else B to storm the sta twins LIMB FRC

Police are be their enquiries b fact that nearly had crowded in the Empire l nesses refuse come forw Burton 'S' said, "I ar faced wi town o' one at face i wer we

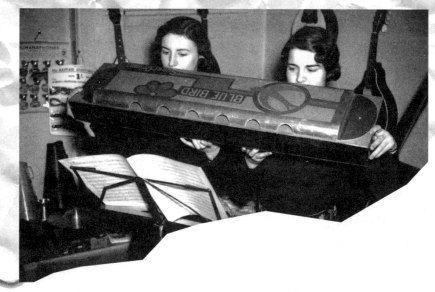

Billy's way of punishing me was to ensure that for the next eighteen months I was unemployable. I had no money and nowhere to live. I suppose I could have moved back in with Mum and Dad but that would have been admitting failure. For a while I lived in a disused chimney in the Old Kent Road; and for six extraordinary weeks in Madame Tussaud's, until my complete inability to remain still for more than seventy-two hours in a row proved to be my eventual undoing. I was caught one night eating a wax effigy of Humphrey Bogart and was kicked out on to the street. Eventually eighteen months to the day since Billy had last contacted me I got an offer of work.

A BBC producer called Giles Moncur was putting together a new show provisionally entitled *Barracks: an Army Comedy*. I was to be one of five featured players, the others being drawn from the ranks of ex-servicemen. Among them was a rather fat young man called Peter Sellers who had recently left the RAF and had been trying to scratch together a living as a jazz drummer. At twenty-four he was some four years older than me but curiously it was I that appeared to be older and wiser. We spent a great deal of time together during the making of *Barracks* and Peter came to think of me as something of a mentor. During one of our many chats at the Lyons Corner House in Shaftesbury Avenue Peter asked me the one question that every performer dreads another performer putting to him. "I'd like some advice," he said. "What direction do you think I should go in? I want to get to the top but I'm not sure there's much mileage in doing funny voices. What do you think, Paul?" I thought long and hard before answering him. A misleading or misguided piece of advice can easily ruin a young performer's future career and I didn't relish being placed in this position. Fortunately on this occasion the answer was blindingly obvious.

"Ditch the funny voices and comedy characters, Peter, there's no future in them. You've got to develop your own distinct personality. That's the only way to survive in this business."

Well, as history records, he ignored my advice completely but I often wonder what great things he might have achieved had he been given his own game show. Still, showbusiness is full of missed opportunities and there's no point in pining over what might have been. Working on *Barracks* gave me the opportunity to meet proper writers for the first time. Alec Winters and Robbie James were young, ambitious, and clearly gifted. I made them like me by being courteous and full of praise for their work. Between the three of us we created the first of

WINTERS & JAMES/BARRACKS/17/24

Scene 1V - The Office

CORPORAL BACKWARDS: You wanted to see me sir!

MAJOR ROADWORKS-AHEAD: Indeed I did Corporal Backwards. Tell me how are things with you XXX at the moment?

CORPORAL BACKWARDS: Perfectly calm sir. One might even say tranquil.

Is this in character?

MAJOR ROADWORKS-AHEAD: I'm very pleased to hear it. Now I want you to go on a secret mission which involves a great deal of XXXXXXX danger and the chances are you'll never come back alive.

CORPORAL BACKWARDS: Joking be must you.

MAJOR ROADWORKS-AHEAD: I've never been more serious.

CORPORAL BACKWARDS: For me take you to idiot of kind what. Blimey.

MAJOR ROADWORKS-AHEAD: Oh this is no good. Corporal I order you to talk backwards deliberately then your words will come out in the XXXXXXX right order. Understood!

CORPORAL BACKWARDS: No. *Alright*

MAJOR ROADWORKS-AHEAD: It's no good saying one word because then I don't know know if you are talking backward, or not.

CORPORAL BACKWARDS: It stuff oh.

34

my comic characters, Corporal Backwards – a soldier inflicted with a rare tropical disease that made him talk backwards whenever he got tense. No tapes exist of the show any more because some nobody wiped them clean but the extract shown on the previous page from the last script of the series should give you some of the flavour.

For a while, "It stuff oh" became one of those catch-phrases that sweep the nation and I certainly wasn't slow on capitalising on it. Novelty records were very big in the early 1950s and my recording of the comedy ballad "It Stuff Oh" remained in the top ten for several weeks. A couple of years ago I was told by his widow Yoko Ono that when John Lennon was six years old "It Stuff Oh" was his favourite song.

It's nice to think that in some small way I could have been personally responsible for all the great Beatles tunes that were recorded over ten years later. At least all the ones that weren't downright odd and peculiar. I have never injected myself with cannabis but if I did perhaps I might appreciate some of their more bizarre songs such as "Colonel Mustard's Lonely Hearts Club Band" for example.

On the basis of one successful radio series and a big hit record I persuaded Mum and Dad to retire to a bungalow in Whitstable. By scraping together every last penny they

had, they somehow managed to afford it. Financially I was in a position to help them but it would only have meant money coming out of my own pocket and I didn't see the sense in that. My parents had always taught self-reliance and it was in that spirit that I hired Alec Winters and Robbie James to be my full-time writers. To my mind, it is better to have someone else being self-reliant for you. *Barracks* had been successful enough but it could hardly be described as my own show. A lot of young comedians were jostling for pole position in the early 1950s and I certainly wasn't going to be left behind. I consulted Billy Castell and he gave me his blessing in the form of a scrappy piece of paper that I found in my trouser pocket one morning.

Nineteen fifty-one proved to be a very big year for me. Not only was my first starring radio series, *Merton's*

A very good idea to work with Winters and James exclusively.Their script will take you back to the top. Be Patient

Madcaps, a huge success but I met the most wonderful girl in the world. Unfortunately at exactly the same time I met the woman who was to become my first wife. My bride to be was called Dulcie Potter. She was nineteen and infatuated with showbusiness. She would sit in the front row of my radio recordings and laugh like a drain and some people said she smelt like one as well. But she suited me because she was everything a showbiz wife should be. Quiet, unassuming, with no ambition at all. So I married her in the summer of 1952. It was a simple ceremony. Just a few friends and thirty-five photographers. The British public have always preferred their entertainers to have solid family values and Dulcie was certainly solid. Helen, my mistress, was an entirely different matter.

I'd met her at the Café de Boulogne, a popular drinking club in the middle of Soho. She was working as a cigarette girl which meant that she wandered around the club dressed as a giant fag while customers attempted to set light to her head. After making some discreet medical enquiries I realised she was all woman. Unbeknownst to Dulcie I bought a two-bedroom flat in Victoria with the proceeds from my hit record and Helen moved in. It was the perfect arrangement all round. My marital home was in Swiss Cottage and to be fair to my wife Dulcie, she made it the perfect setting for me to go to once I'd been

*Dulcie Potter, my first wife, was a plain girl and contrasted a
great deal with my mistress of the time, Helen (see plate section).
But I loved her.*

sexually satisfied elsewhere. It was cosy, clean and dull. Dulcie always understood that if a radio recording overran I would spend the night in a hotel rather than disturb her at two o'clock in the morning. Luckily an extraordinary number of recordings "overran" and on every single occasion I stayed the night with Helen.

Of course it was a dangerous game but for the first two years Dulcie didn't suspect a thing. Who knows how long this state of bliss would have continued if my wife hadn't seen me, quite by chance, one February morning passionately kissing Helen in the back of a taxi. But for that one piece of unfortunate bad luck I'm sure I would never have contemplated separation from Dulcie. And I certainly wouldn't have murdered her. It really was the only option open to me. When I got home that night Dulcie flew into the most extraordinary rage. She accused me of cheating on her.

I was told that I was not a proper husband, whatever that might mean, and I was threatened with a big fat messy divorce. Stars did not get divorced in the mid-1950s. It was a family industry and marital problems were the kiss of death. So that very night I strangled her with a silk tie that had been presented to me by the Variety Club of Great Britain for the Best Radio Newcomer of 1952. I don't suppose she felt a thing. I drove for several hours that night with her body in the boot of the car. I dropped her down a disused tin mine near Truro. She had no family to speak of apart from a rather simple brother whom I had forbidden Dulcie ever to contact again, shortly after we were first married. I don't like meeting ordinary people at the best of times and he was a greengrocer! Ordinary people suck the artistic imagination out of creative artistes and this brother was a right sod for doing just that. So because wives were expected to stay in the background nobody ever noticed that Dulcie wasn't there any more. She never attended radio recordings after our marriage anyway and after a few months of not seeing her around people simply forgot that she had ever existed. Shortly after, Helen left for America as the new face of Estée Lauder.

By 1956 *Merton's Madcaps* was the most popular radio show of its day. Its fast-paced dialogue and bizarre characters made me a household name. Around about this time I met Tony Hancock who was also making a career for himself. He was sitting in the Hand and Racket pub with his two writers Alan Simpson and Roy Galton. They seemed nervous of my star status and it's a great pity I suppose that I never got the chance to work with them. I know that I certainly impressed Tony with my show-business anecdotes. After a few hours of talking to him

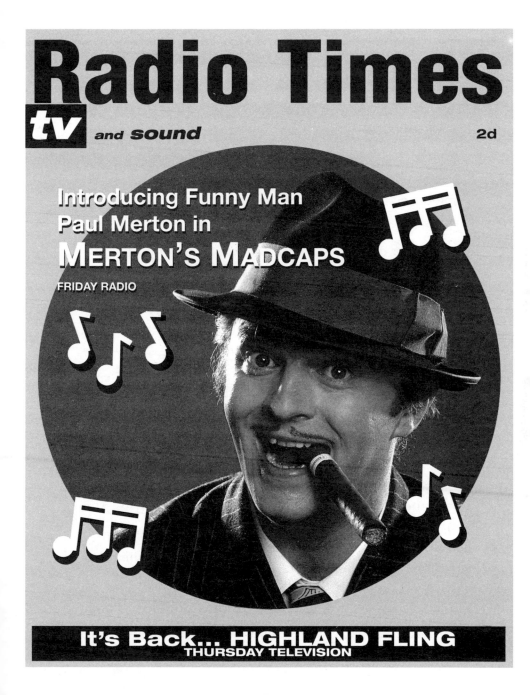

non-stop he suddenly interrupted by saying, "What a fascinating man you are."

I count that as one of the greatest tributes that I've ever been paid in this business. The success of *Merton's Madcaps* led to my first major film role in over twenty years. It was an Ealing film, one of the very last to be produced by the studio that had enthralled the world with a succession of highly successful movies. In one of the accounts of the history of Ealing Studios my film *The Ironmonger* was singled out as the production that finally bankrupted the company. If that means I played some part in the emergence of the new wave in British cinema that occurred at the very end of the 1950s then I'm more than happy to take all the credit. *The Ironmonger* was a very popular film in its day and broke box office records all over the country but unfortunately the production costs ran completely over budget. If the film had been successful in America, Ealing would no doubt have made a handsome profit but unfortunately as a title *The Ironmonger* meant nothing in the States. Stupidly the Americans changed its name to *Man of Steel* which led audiences to expect a super-hero with special powers battling against evil geniuses bent on world domination. Instead they got a rather simple story of a man selling brass hooks in Lewisham.

Although *The Ironmonger* had lost money I was heralded in some quarters as the new face to watch. I was contacted by a film cameraman called F. Stop Fitzgerald who was keen to direct his first movie. As an unknown director nobody wanted to take a chance on him but I accepted his offer, confident that my know-how would get us out of any trouble. Well, the film we made became a huge international hit. Everywhere! It was called *The Ladybirds* and was about a Salvation Army band shipwrecked on a desert island that is being used by the British to test the atomic bomb. The subsequent radiation levels cause the castaways to mutate into a curious mixture of human and insect until one day they simply fly off the island and return to civilisation. Back in London the mutants are initially greeted with revulsion but they eventually win people over with a well choreographed song-and-dance routine celebrating the wonders of the atomic age. A review in the *Daily Sketch* accurately captured the mood of the film. "*The Ladybirds*, with its enchanting storyline and highly skilled performances clearly proves that the world has no reason to fear nuclear weapons and this positive outlook makes the film an absolute joy for family audiences everywhere. Over-exposure to deadly radiation has never been such fun."

Much to everybody's amazement *The Ladybirds* was a massive hit in America. Personally I couldn't understand it. It was as if we'd had some giant publicity machine at our disposal but we didn't. I was inundated with offers to appear on American television. And once people think you're a big film star, you become a big film star. I appeared on the Ed Sullivan TV show along with a then relatively unknown singer called Elvis Presley, and my appearance alone guaranteed record viewing figures. An enterprising journalist working for *Time* Magazine did some research and wrote an in-depth profile of me under the headline "Whatever happened to Baby Paul?" My earlier Hollywood films were re-released and proved exceptionally popular with the teen generation. The response was so fantastic that Paramount Pictures offered me an exclusive contract to make fifteen films over a ten-year period. An offer which I readily accepted.

I had no qualms about leaving Britain behind. Shortly after settling in America I met the woman who was to become my second wife. I'd been invited to a party held by the British Ambassador in Washington. As I looked around the Embassy I couldn't help but be impressed by the cut-glass chandeliers, the deep pile carpet and the Old Masters hanging on every wall. I fell into conversation with one of the Old Masters who told me that he was a former headteacher of Eton College and that the Ambassador liked the sheer Englishness of having first-class educators dangling above the fireplace. The Ambassador himself was friendly and greeted me with the words, "Well we've managed to make a success out of you." Although puzzled by the remark initially, I later assumed that he was simply expressing patriotic pride at my success in America.

And then I saw her.

My wife to be.

Barbara Rothschild was rich, elegant, beautiful and rich. Her personal fortune exceeded the combined financial assets of Europe. She fell in love with my accent immediately and I, in my own way, fell in love with her. We got married and on the occasion of our first wedding anniversary in 1960 my darling Barbara bought me Portugal for my own personal use. Always photographed at every high-society occasion, we became the most famous couple in America and therefore the world. We lived in the biggest mansion in Washington. Very much a woman of her time, Barbara was very keen on all kinds of modern scientific gadgets and so our house was full of them. All the kitchen appliances, for example, reacted to spoken commands. If you placed a chicken in the oven and said "Cook" in a loud voice the oven would automatically cook the bird. Other gadgets reacted to mere vowel sounds. In the living-room you only had to utter a contented "Ahhh" sound as you sat back into the sofa to conjure up a labrador, a log fire and a balloon of vintage brandy from behind a curtain. Yes, we were happy. My first film for Paramount was a huge financial success and at thirty years old I was on top of the world.

As I sit here watching the afternoon sun disappearing behind the orange groves that are a spectacular feature of my luxurious Spanish villa, it gives me tremendous satisfaction to relive the golden memories of those halcyon years. Belinda, my fifth wife, has still not returned home, however. Being of Latin temperament she struggles with the concept of punctuality but of course I love her dearly. I don't get on with her side of the family, so I'd much rather she visited her sister in Argentina on her own. Better that than have me endure the idiotic rantings of my brother-in-law who seems to believe that belching is an Olympic sport judging by the amount of practice he puts into it. And also it would be extremely dangerous for me to leave the country. I long ago got used to the idea that I will die in Spain. Even if I don't, one thing's for certain, I'll never set foot in Britain again. Still, I dare say my wife will turn up shortly full of apologies and vodka. She's nervous of air travel, poor thing, and drinks excessively to knock herself out for the flight.

My film career went from strength to strength. In 1961 I received an Oscar nomination in the Best Actor category for my performance as a Cornish smuggler providing illicit alcohol to a tiny village. I loved that film and always thought its title *Rum Cove* was a clever play on words. In 1962 for our third wedding anniversary I bought Barbara the world's most expensive diamond. The Raj stone was impossible to insure and so we kept it in a large safe lined with the softest velvet but we made sure that everyone knew we had it. Occasionally honoured guests were allowed to look at an X-ray of the safe with the diamond showing up as a dark lump in the middle.

In 1963 came an emotional time for me – I was voted the biggest international film star in the world by the readers of *Sprocket Holes* magazine. There was no doubt that everybody in the world loved me. I don't think anyone would have blamed me for thinking that it would last for ever.

But it didn't.

Chapter 4

In 1964 my past returned to haunt me. As many of you know an obscure publication that I won't even deign to name here, printed details of my wartime efforts to entertain the Nazis but the subtleties of my true valour in the war completely passed them by. Within a matter of days it was front-page stuff all over the world and the fickle press made mincemeat of me. The state of Israel immediately banned all my films and staged a trial which found me guilty of collaboration with the enemy. Sentence was handed down and I was executed in my absence and although patently absurd, the ruling was supported by international law and I was officially pronounced dead.

This meant that although I was still clearly alive I was in fact, to all intents and purposes, non-existent. Nobody was allowed to talk to me or acknowledge my presence in any way. Because I was "dead" my wIfe Barbara received all my worldly assets according to the terms of my will and to add insult to injury she changed all the locks to all the doors in our Hollywood mansion in case I should attempt to "haunt" her from beyond the grave. Being dead ruined my life. It was impossible to get a good table in a restaurant, not even one by the door. I was penniless and friendless, and even Douglas Fairbanks Junior, whom I'd

SHOCK! PAUL LOVES THE NAZIS

NAZI きしむ下に PAUL すき 北

כדוטף PAUL ב י ח־ NAZI

PAUL ATE NAZI'S HAMSTER

रफज०ऱ्ट्ज़्व PAUL ढ़र तफ NAZIS

ௗழட PAUL ஜ௬ற NAZI

PAUL ADORE LE NAZIS!

A collection of the headlines that said only one thing to me –
International Death Sentence.

come to regard as a friend, cut me dead in the super-market. I tried to contact my widow on several occasions until a message was relayed to me, through an exceed-ingly roundabout route, that it was considered the height of social disgrace to accept telephone calls from a corpse. The rest of America shunning me I could understand. There is a strong Jewish lobby in American politics and their concerns have to be addressed. But for my ex-wife to behave as if the person she had known and loved had somehow died with me, was too much to bear.

And so I killed her.

One night I broke into the house and bludgeoned her to death with the Honorary Oscar presented to me by the Academy for my "rare skills in bringing joy to the world". I reasoned that if I couldn't enjoy my worldly goods then neither could she. Of course being dead I couldn't be charged with her murder. I left America a penniless non-citizen and arrived back at London airport just before Christmas 1964. It was almost exactly thirty years to the day since I had first returned from Hollywood in absolute disgrace and here I was going through the same old routine again. At least Britain's relationship with Israel wasn't as close as the Americans' and upon my arrival I was immediately arrested by customs for flying without a valid ticket. At the American end I had simply wandered on to the plane, ignored by all the airline officials. Once it had been established that I was a British citizen and that Pan Am had no record of me ever having been on their flight, however, I was released without charge.

I spent Christmas with my parents in their neo-Georgian bungalow in Whitstable. It was fun to do simple family things again and I was surprised by how much I enjoyed watching them put up all the decorations, preparing the Christmas turkey and dealing with the mountains of washing up afterwards. Over that holiday period I spent a great deal of time thinking about my future. I was thirty-four years old and had spent my entire life in showbusiness. Did I have the stamina to relaunch my career in Britain? Was it really worth climbing back on to that insane roller-coaster? Dad recommended that I contact Billy Castell. After all, my troubles always occurred when I was out of the country and away from his circle of influence. My two trips to America and my cabaret work in Berlin had all ended disastrously so perhaps there was a lesson to be learnt.

As per the usual manner I placed an advert in Dalton's Weekly and awaited Billy's response. The gist of his reply, which incidentally was written in chalk on a brick wall near my parent's home, was that it might well be a good idea to take a break from the business and had I

*I spent a happy Xmas day kissing my mistress Helen under the mistletoe in 1953.
She is pictured here in our love nest in London's Victoria.*

PAUL MERTON

**Star of Radio's 'Barracks' and the voice
behind the popular song "It Stuff Oh"**

Available for Radio, Television, Light Entertainment

Agent: Billy Castell

*1950 was a big year for me. My role as Corporal Backwards in the
radio show 'Barracks' pushed me back into the public spotlight.*

*The Ladybirds was a fantastic film and a world-wide phenomenon.
I am pictured here in my lead role as a Salvation Army Captain.*

You're The Mugs
You're The Mugs
You're The Mugs
You're The Mugs
You're The Mugs
You're The Mugs
You're The Mugs
You're The Mugs
You're The Mugs

You're The Mugs
A MiddleEngland Production
Nationwide at 8.00pm every Sunday
Starring Paul Merton
Directed by Helen Freeman
For interviews and press packs please contact
Cato Buchan on 0171 xxxx number

You haven't hit the big time until you've hosted a top ITV game show.

I went through a great deal of unpleasentness in the name of Charity in the 1960s. It was worth it though.

41, Bedford Road

This picture documents the happy day that I joined the Royal Variety Club of Great Britain. After the fiasco with Augustine the hippo, my membership was revoked.

In all my life I was never happier than when I was exploring London's secret underground network of tunnels. I took the picture above with an automatic camera to celebrate my 50th birthday.

*I've come a long way since Carlisle in 1931. My new show, Happy Hour,
is breaking new boundaries on satellite television.*

considered the possibility of running a small antiques shop in East Sussex? As on countless previous occasions Billy had correctly judged my mood and was pointing me towards the future. Because I had so much time on my hands I started thinking about the extraordinary phenomenon that was Billy Castell. He'd represented the family for nearly forty years but none of us knew what he looked like or sounded like or even how old he was. Why did he conduct business in such an unusual manner? Why bother chalking a message on a wall when it would be so much simpler to send a postcard? Why was a teapot thrown at me in Tottenham Court Road and how, back in the 1930s, did Billy manage to place a message on the B-side of a gramophone record informing my father that Baby Paul was booked into the London Palladium? At the time Dad assumed the voice belonged to Billy but we've had no proof of that. And exactly how did he manage to persuade King George V to rehearse the act for several weeks?

Dozens of questions and only one way to answer them. I decided to find Billy Castell. *Dalton's Weekly* seemed a good place to start. I made an appointment to see George Thomas, the managing director of *Dalton's Weekly*, and travelled to London to meet him. I concocted a story about wanting to make a feature film set in their offices.

Working on the assumption that ordinary people knew nothing about showbusiness, I bamboozled George Thomas with spurious detail and erroneous information until I had him eating out of the palm of my hand.

"We very much see this film as an international block-buster," I told him. "A murder is committed and the managing director of *Dalton's Weekly* sets out to find the killer but soon stumbles into a web of intrigue."

"A web of intrigue," repeated Mr Thomas. "That sounds very interesting."

"Oh it is," I said. "And we see Cary Grant playing you. And Alfred Hitchcock will direct it."

"Alfred Hitchcock," he said. "That would be wonderful."

"Of course it has to be authentic," I continued. "Mr Hitchcock would insist upon it. We must get every detail right. The murderer places adverts in the second-hand fridge section of *Dalton's Weekly* so obviously we need to do some research in that direction."

"Second-hand fridge section," repeated Mr Thomas in a somewhat bemused fashion.

"Yes, and Michael Caine's going to be in it."

"Michael Caine!"

"Yes, and Elizabeth Taylor." I was deliberately giving him no time to think. "Take this advert for example," I said producing a recent copy of *Dalton's Weekly* with one of Billy's messages ringed in blue ink. "Who placed it and where do they live?"

George Thomas took the magazine from me. "Oh, this is one of Billy Castell's," he said. "I believe he's a theatrical agent."

I feigned amazement. "Billy Castell! I haven't seen him for years. Where's he living these days?"

"I'll check the files," he said and spoke to his secretary via the intercom. Within thirty-five seconds she entered the office clutching a piece of paper. I resisted the enormous temptation to grab it off her and run out of the building laughing manically.

"We send all his bills to number 34b Goldhawk Road. Tell me, is there any chance that I could meet Miss Taylor?"

He wittered on in this vein for some time but I was too stunned to take any notice. 34b Goldhawk Road. Mum and Dad's second-hand shop had been at 34a Goldhawk Road. Could Billy really have been a neighbour of ours?

I thanked George Thomas and promised that MGM would be in touch within the hour. I left the building and caught a taxi to the Goldhawk Road. Twenty-five minutes later I stood outside Mum and Dad's old shop which was now an off-licence. The number above the door read 34a.

The shops on either side of the off-licence were numbered 32 and 36. So where was 34b? I stood on the pavement wondering what on earth I was going to do next when I saw a postman walking towards me. "34b, mate?" he said "It's round the back. Take the next road on the left, follow that until you reach an alleyway. Go down the alleyway past three huge dustbins and it's the door on your left."

I thanked him, walked round the corner, down the alleyway, past the three huge dustbins and saw a door marked 34b and 34c. I pushed it open and found a staircase directly in front of me. Fighting the impulse to run up it two at a time, I grabbed the bannister, took a deep breath and walked up the stairs in the most nonchalant manner I could muster. As I climbed upwards I silently rehearsed my opening remark. "Ah, Mr Castell, we meet at last." No – that sounded like a line from a cheap spy novel. By the top of the stairs I had settled on the rather unimaginative "Hello, Billy". The door at the top was marked Gosport Travel. This didn't bother me because knowing Billy's love of secrecy I hardly expected it to read "Castell's Theatrical Agency Don't Bother to Knock". I pushed through the door and found a middle-aged Indian man sitting behind a grubby desk. The walls were covered with maps of the world and travel brochures were scattered all over the room. I glanced around looking for a door that clearly wasn't there. "I'm looking for 34b," I said.

"It's back downstairs" replied the man. "Immediately to the left of the front door as you come in." I went back down the stairs and there it was, 34b. I knocked on the door but nobody answered. I tried the handle but it was locked. The front door opened behind me and the postman entered. "I see you found it then," he said pushing a couple of envelopes through the letter-box. "Yes," I said thinking quickly. "I'm from *Dalton's Weekly*. We haven't heard from Mr Castell for a few weeks, and I was just checking that he hadn't changed address or anything like that. See much of him?" I said hoping to trap the postman into some detailed description of what Billy looked like.

"Never set eyes on him, mate," he replied as he climbed the stairs towards Gosport Travel. "If you're worried about him why don't you write him a letter?" Which of course was the very last thing I should do. Having found Billy's office it hardly made sense to let him know I was on his trail. I wanted to meet him or at least talk to him. I resolved to find his telephone number.

In 1965 London was beginning to swing. Young people had money to spend and the shops were full of daring new fashions. Apparently there was a fresh spirit of

*Kensington High Street, 1965, just moments away from my
parents' old shop in Goldhawk Rd. As you can see, London was
beginning to swing but I saw none of it – I spent the year tracking
down Billy Castell.*

optimism in the air. But I missed it all. For all I knew, policemen were tapdancing in Trafalgar Square and the Prime Minister was handing out free money to anyone who had a big smile on their face. I missed it all because I spent the majority of 1965 tracking down Billy Castell's phone number.

First I moved out of my parent's bungalow in Whitstable and rented a tiny bedsit that was frankly disgusting but at least had the advantage of being near the Goldhawk Road. Now how exactly do you discover somebody's ex-directory telephone number? Well, in short this is how I did it.

Directory Enquiries told me that Gosport Travel's telephone number was 43 8724. I felt safe in assuming that Billy's number would begin with the same two digits. Now I had to find the last four numbers. There are ten thousand possible variants of a four-figure number, so I got hold of a London telephone directory and crossed out every single number listed without a 43 prefix. This reduced the possible combinations to eight hundred and seven. I dialled each one of these numbers in turn. On some I got a line-disconnected tone so I immediately eliminated them from the list. On others if there was no answer after a minute I would make a note of the number in my 'to be phoned back' column. For those numbers who answered I pretended to be a telephone engineer: "I'm sorry to disturb you, it's the telephone engineer here. We've had a couple of reports that Gosport Travel's phone line is constantly engaged, I wonder if you could pop upstairs and ask them to replace their receiver correctly?" A simple enough request designed to confuse everybody but Billy Castell. And everyone I spoke to on the phone was confused. None had heard of Gosport Travel and the vast majority volunteered the information that I had got through to a private residence and if there was a travel agent's upstairs they were certainly being very quiet about it. Finally after just a few months I reduced the list to fifteen numbers. Fifteen numbers that nobody answered no matter what time I phoned them day or night. From there it was easy.

I went to a telephone box just down the road from Billy's office and dialled the first number. I left the phone dangling off its receiver, came out of the phone box, walked down the alleyway, pushed through the door marked 34b and 34c and placed my ear to the door of Billy's office. There was no phone ringing. I went back to the phone box, dialled another number and repeated the process. Finally phone number twelve came through. I dialed 43 8432, made my way back to the office and heard Billy's phone ringing through the door.

43

8318
8396
8397
8401
8402
8424
8410
8417
8419
8420
8421
8431
8433
8432
8442
8443
8447
8451
8461
8461

43 9862
8477
8479
8480
8481
8482
8489
8490
8492
8505
8510
8511
8533
8534
8542
8544
8582
8594
8596
8602

Success! Well success of sorts. For the following month I phoned Billy's number every twenty minutes. I sometimes even set the alarm clock for three in the morning just to wake me up to call Billy. But the phone just rang and rang.

Finally, out of sheer frustration, I took the law into my own hands. In the early hours of 29th September I pushed past the three huge dustbins and shoulder-charged the door marked 34b and 34c. I kicked the lock in on Billy's door, pushed it open, switched on the light and found myself standing in a slightly larger than average cupboard. The walls were bare. The only item of furniture was a small stool with a telephone placed on top of it. Under the telephone was this typed written note addressed to me.

I glanced back to the top of the page and then looked at my watch. It was 2.25 a.m. The top of the page was marked 2.15 a.m. How could Billy know I would break into his office on 29th September, and how could he predict to the nearest ten minutes the exact time? This man was amazing.

Instead of solving the mystery I had created another larger mystery. All I'd done was to waste several months tracking down a phone number that was no good to me at all. I went back to the bedsit, drank three stiff whiskies and a limp cognac. I didn't sleep well for the rest of that night.

2.15am

Hello Paul,

Well its nearly a year since your return from Hollywood and I'm glad you took my advice and decided to take some time off from the business. Commercial television wants you to host a brand new game show. A man called Justin Wheeler will contact you tommorow.

Best regards, Billy

Chapter 5

Justin Wheeler telephoned me at 10.30 the following morning. ITV wanted me to host a brand new game show called *You're The Mugs*. The idea which was very popular at the time was to stage elaborate hoaxes on members of the public and film their reactions with hidden cameras. On one occasion I remember we told a couple they had been left half a million pounds by a relative they had never heard of. We drove them to London and they met a bogus solicitor who confirmed every detail. They were then encouraged to go on a spending spree for several days until finally we broke the news that not only was there no inheritance but they had also run up a debt of fifteen thousand pounds! At this point as they did every week the rest of the family emerged from behind a curtain to humiliate the unfortunate couple by shouting in unison, "You're The Mugs!".

With a mixture of different hoaxes every week *You're The Mugs* proved to be a great hit with the general public and I was voted ITV Personality of the Year for 1966.

I was kept busy throughout that year and the next so I really didn't spend much time thinking about Billy Castell and that strange little office-cum-cupboard of his. My domestic situation also took a distinct turn for the better.

I moved out of the bedsit and into a three-bedroomed ground-floor mansion flat just behind the British Museum. And I married the hostesss of *You're The Mugs*, a charming young lady called Melissa who satisfied my every need. We were photographed everywhere together, first nights, West End restaurants, switching on the Christmas lights in Regent Street; we became one of the showbiz couples of the sixties. I was flooded with requests for various charities but it was impossible to say yes to everybody so I concentrated on the causes that were most likely to get me an OBE. Children and animals are usually a good bet and so in 1967 I became life president of the Blind Dogs for the Guides Society. An obscure organisation whose chief aim is to supply blind dogs to girl guides. Apparently it teaches the little darlings responsibility, but it meant very little work for me and loads of personal publicity so I was happy to go along with it all.

At first, life at home with Melissa was everything it should be. We entertained Heads of State every other weekend and soon our gin rummy night became the talk of the Commonwealth. But behind the jolly public façade trouble was brewing. I'd first started to drink heavily in 1965. Sitting in a bedsit all day crossing numbers out of a phone book isn't much fun unless you do it with a bottle of Scotch inside you. Perhaps I should make clear that it was the contents that were inside me rather than the bottle itself. I'd hate to conjure up any unnecessarily crude imagery. And so with wealth at my finger-tips I slowly succumbed to the powers of drink.

One of my favourite drinking clubs was Happy Sam's, a tiny little place tucked behind a small courtyard in Soho. Membership was only offered to those people whose photograph had appeared on the front cover of the *TV Times*. I was proud to be part of that select group. Amongst my regular drinking companions was Aleister Crowley, the notorious satanist. He'd featured on the cover of *TV Times* in 1963 to publicise his role as guest commentator for that year's FA Cup Final. Unfortunately

Happy Sams

MEMBERSHIP CARD

Name *P. Merton*   No   *728*

If you're not famous you're not welcome

TV TIMES/6d

F.A.CUP FINAL SPECIAL
Guest commentator Aleister Crowley

Manchester United vs Leicester City
Brought to you live on the big day
with Dickie Davis and Aleister Crowley

Inside:
Behind the scenes
on Drama 63 and
Armchair Theatre

The return
of Max Bygraves

Kennedy's Funeral

Kathy McGowan SPECIAL

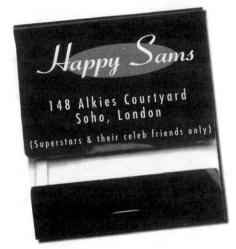

the self-proclaimed Master of the Black Arts had a very shaky knowledge of the off-side rule and so was quietly dropped the following year. I always found Aleister a completely charming man who loved nothing better than reading out the jokes printed on the back of matchboxes. I knew that millions regarded him as the Spawn of Beelzebub but you know how people like to gossip. I didn't realise that he had in fact died in 1947, but being satanic he could shrug off this minor detail.

Some nights I wouldn't get home from Happy Sam's until five o'clock in the morning. I would spin Melissa some yarn about falling asleep on a chair somewhere and for a while she believed me. But my regular nightly excursions into Soho gave her the perfect opportunity to sit at home and think.

Although we were the perfect showbiz couple, in financial terms we were far from being equal. On *You're The Mugs* I was paid a star's salary while Melissa was paid a hostess's salary. Absolutely fair, I'm sure you'll agree, but she didn't see it that way. No matter how gently I put it to her, she could never understand that her position in the show was that of an empty-headed blonde who could be replaced at the drop of a hat. I suppose if I had been home more in the evenings I could have dealt with the problem more diplomatically by telling her to shut up every five minutes. But I didn't. I was spending every available night in Happy Sam's. Behind my back Melissa negotiated a contract with the BBC to star in her very own chat show. The first I knew about it was the morning after the first programme had been broadcast. I've never been an avid newspaper reader and because I was out every night I wasn't seeing any television either. A taxi driver broke the news to me.

"Your wife's show is a bloody disgrace."

I asked him what he was talking about and he showed me the first page of the *Daily Mirror*. "Funny Man's Wife is Rubbish" read the headline. Well you can imagine the shock. It's never a good move to be associated with failure in this business and to be married to it is a cardinal sin. I directed the cab back to my house and confronted Melissa in the kitchen. She was totally unrepentant. She didn't seem to care tuppence about my career and instead kept going on about the unfairness of the press.

Then she dropped the bombshell.

"Where would your precious career be if people knew you were out drinking with Aleister Crowley every night?" There was a silence between us. We both perfectly understood the nature of the threat. My status as the country's foremost family entertainer would be placed in severe jeopardy. I had to think quickly. I apologised to Melissa immediately and agreed that I had behaved abysmally towards her. I promised to stand by her no matter what the press said about her new show. And although I didn't have to, I agreed that we should be paid exactly the same money on the next series of *You're The Mugs*. I made all these promises in the sure knowledge that I would never have to keep them. Because of course I had already made the decision to kill her.

This was becoming a habit.

As luck would have it Melissa died in a fatal car crash the next day so I didn't have to bother. A mentally unbalanced choreographer called Tommy Whitehaven had been so incensed by Melissa's chat show that he had

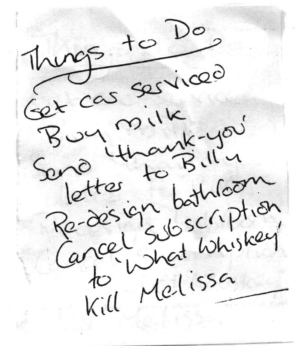

taken it upon himself to drain the brake fluid out of her car. By an extraordinary piece of bad luck when Melissa completely failed to stop at the traffic lights by Tottenham Court Road underground station she actually knocked Tommy Whitehaven over before being hit full square by a double-decker bus. The whole sequence of events would have remained a total mystery if I hadn't, by sheer chance, been walking past at the time of the accident. I was the first person to reach Tommy Whitehaven and I just wish to God that somebody other than me had heard him confess to his crime before he passed away.

The inquest was very upsetting, particularly as all the cameramen outside seemed to take a perverse pleasure in photographing my face from the wrong angle. The funeral itself, however, was a splendid occasion and I think we did Melissa proud. It was certainly the finest send-off for a quiz show hostess that *this* country has ever seen. We made one more series of *You're The Mugs* but the British public didn't take to Melissa's replacement too well and after five successful years we decided to call it a day. However the drinking continued. Occasionally I thought of contacting Alcoholics Anonymous but I couldn't find their phone number anywhere, so so much for anonymity. I suppose I drank because doing a quiz show for five years was financially rewarding but hardly represented a

A Memorial Service

for Melissa

❀

Prayers of Rememberance

Reading from Biblical Texts

Hynm Number 458

Personal Tribute Reading

Last Rites

Now appearing as Melissa's replacement in the hit show
"You're The Mugs", Tania Malone 'the hostess with the mostess'

challenge any more. In the past I had been a famous actor but in 1973 I was chiefly known as the man in a three-piece suit who humiliated people for the purposes of light entertainment.

My career desperately needed a new direction so I placed an advert in *Dalton's Weekly*. Billy's reply told me to contact the head of BBC sit-com as soon as possible. The BBC wanted me to play the part of a big game hunter living in Nairobi who shot loads of lions and was rude to his servants. I didn't like the big game hunter, Nairobi, lions and servants element but apart from that it sounded great. Thanks to my comments it eventually mutated into a comedy about a very tall angry man with a moustache running a hotel in Torquay. But I never shared in the programme's success. By now my life was desperate. I hadn't been on television for almost a year and I was in danger of being forgotten. I was offered the occasional game show which only confirmed that I had made the cardinal mistake of getting myself typecast.

My predicament brought to mind an American character actor I'd met in Hollywood in the early 1960s. His name was Willard Glengoso and he had first leapt to prominence with his portrayal of 'The Beast' in the film *The Beast From 50,000 Fathoms*. If ever a man was born to act inside a green rubberised suit it was Willard. Such was his impact in the movie that he was flooded with offers to appear in all kinds of films, on the strict understanding that all his scenes would feature him in a green rubberised suit. If you've ever wondered who the huge reptile is serenading Audrey Hepburn in *My Fair Lady*, now you know.

But soon the novelty wore off and Willard was reduced to making guest appearances in shoddy American soap operas. Eventually he went mad and was shot down from an aeroplane while attempting to climb the Empire State Building. Showbiz is littered with a thousand such casualties and unless I got the break I needed, I was destined to become one of them.

But salvation came in the most unexpected form. Totally out of the blue I was awarded an OBE in the Queen's New Year Honours List.

What a result! Blind Dogs and Girl Guides had suddenly kicked in. When one embarks on charity work it's always heartwarming to see a positive result at the end, and what could be more uplifting than an OBE? I appeared in all the papers the following day. I was interviewed by News at Ten and the Nine o'Clock News, which helped to firmly remind the British public about how much they loved me. People stopped me in the street and shook me by the hand. Through the warmth, generosity and the hero worship of others I began putting my life back into some sort of order. I managed to keep the drinking under some sort of control for many years after that. Although still addicted I couldn't bear the idea of jeopardising my respectable image by allowing my fans to see me walking down Oxford Street stinking of booze and covered in vomit. And a lot of people in my business share the same attitude.

In April 1974 I went to Buckingham Palace to receive my award from the Queen. I was proud to take my place amongst the lifeboat rescuemen and ex-football managers. A lot of people criticise the honours system but generally speaking those people don't have OBEs, so I'm sure it's sour grapes on their part.

It's well known that the Queen is adept at putting people at their ease and after discussing different types of water with the lifeboatman standing alongside she eventually turned her attention to me. She was gracious enough to say how much she enjoyed my work and that as far as she was concerned *You're The Mugs* described perfectly the monarchy's role within the British constitution. I wasn't quite sure what she meant by this but I smiled politely and then ignored her.

A few minutes later, however, I found myself talking to Prince Charles and we hit it off immediately.To my surprise he was a huge fan of my radio show in the 1950s. He told me that he particularly liked the character of Corporal Backwards and he then went on to say that in his experience 'the character did not exclusively belong to the world of fiction'.

He paused with a smile playing about his lips and for a moment I wasn't quite sure how I was supposed to react. And then to my left I noticed a footman holding up a white card with "LAUGH" written on it. This cued warm and generous laughter around the room and I was happy to join in with it although for the life of me I didn't know what we were supposed to be laughing at. Prince Charles continued, "And I can assure you that backwardness as a characteristic is not entirely confined to the rank of Corporal within the British Army." I noticed everybody's eyes flickering across to the footman who duly produced the white card and we all once again laughed uproari-ously. I was beginning to get the hang of this and so after a few more minutes of conversation I boldly attempted a joke of my own. "It strikes me, Your Majesty, that if some of our generals are backward that can only be a good thing. At least we can detect some kind of movement from them." This remark was met by total silence. I nudged the footman to my left but no white card was produced. All eyes were on the Prince. To my relief he

"How do you start a Pudding Race? Say Go! Do you get it?"

eventually chuckled, then giggled and finally roared with laughter. The footman displayed the white card and everybody else joined in. When the merriment subsided Prince Charles shook me by the hand, told me that I was "a most amusing fellow" and would I be free to dine with him that evening. I of course accepted.

I dined with Prince Charles on several occasions throughout 1974 and we became firm friends. Reports of our regular dinners together quickly filtered into the upper echelons of society. Soon I was invited to dine with the aristocracy in all the most fashionable houses in London. The majority of people I met had never heard of *You're The Mugs* and some of them even denied there was such a thing as ITV. I was purely accepted on the grounds that I regularly dined with Prince Charles, which just goes to show how unsnobbish these people really are. I became close friends with the Marchmont family and their youngest daughter in particular. Emily was nineteen years old and the epitome of the English rose. She had a big red face that used to bloom every summer. She was enchanted by my stories about the variety theatre, which was so far removed from her everyday experience. I might as well have been talking about Manchester. I loved the charming way she described all those below her on the social scale as 'losers'.

On 14th Febuary 1975 we announced our engagement to be married. Now that I was moving in such exalted circles I desperately needed the huge income that goes hand in hand with a hit television show. I placed an advert in *Dalton's Weekly* and awaited Billy's response. I was rather hoping that he might suggest something up market along the lines of *Paul Merton's Guide to English Stately Butlers*, so I was rather disappointed to receive a call from ITV offering me a brand new game show called *Lucky Beggars*.

The idea of this one was that the programme would celebrate people who had enjoyed a great deal of luck in their lives. We would tell their individual stories and then the studio audience would vote for the person that they believed fully deserved a plastic horse-shoe with the words 'Lucky Beggar' stencilled on the back. I liked the idea chiefly because nothing else was being offered to me and so I signed a contract and we immediately embarked on a series of sixty-five shows. ITV wanted more, but in my experience, if you record more than sixty-five in any one go it's impossible to keep the standard up. We recorded thirteen shows a day and finished the series in a week.

I married Emily on 25th October 1975. We spent our honeymoon in the penthouse suite of the Dorchester

Hotel, taking pot-shots at commuters with a high-powered air rifle. After the honeymoon I recorded another series of *Lucky Beggars* and we then settled down to married life in my ground-floor mansion flat behind the British Museum. We quickly became the society couple. We attended all the high-class functions and found ourselves dining out every single night. This saved us a great deal of money and we didn't have to worry about the washing-up. Despite riding the social merry-go-round I still found time to visit Prince Charles on a regular basis.

You *are warmly invited to thoroughly 'pig-out' at*

The Pringle-Hennessey-Jones's Soirée

on 15th July at 8pm

R.S.V.P.

Dress Formal

*You are cordially invited to
come for some nosh with*

The Sambard-Chapman-Daws

*on 23rd April at 8pm
Dress Formal
R S V P*

On one such evening after sharing a particularly fine bottle of Amontillado, Charles dismissed the footman and his white card with "laugh" written on it, which I took to mean that our previous, frivolous, conversation was about to take a serious turn. My instinct was correct. I don't know if you've ever seen a grown man sobbing uncontrollably. I certainly hadn't and neither had Prince Charles so we talked about something else.

The conversation that followed was to change my life.

According to the Prince rumours had circulated among the Royal Family for years about the possible existence of an elaborate system of tunnels underneath London. "Yes,"

I wanted to say. "It's called the Picccadilly Line," but as the man with the white card had left, there didn't seem to be any point. The Prince then went on to tell me that according to legend these secret tunnels had been built just after the turn of the century on the express wishes of Edward VII. Apparently he loved to travel around the capital in total secrecy and because he was the King nobody had the nerve to tell him that it was a stupid idea that would cost billions. But the British Empire was at the height of its wealth and apparently the tunnels were built. Charles then explained that the reason why he was telling me this was because of a persistent rumour that a tunnel definitely existed between Buckingham Palace and a certain ground-floor flat behind the British Museum. His words had exactly the desired effect on me.

"Would this ground-floor flat be situated at 41 Bedford Road?" I asked.

"It would," he replied. "Your own flat, of course. If such a tunnel exists it would be easier to locate it at your end rather than search under the floorboards here at the Palace. We have ninety-three rooms on the ground floor alone."

"I see. Are you suggesting, Your Highness, that I should go home tonight and rip the floorboards up?" I said.

"Oh no, no," replied the Prince. "I mention it in case

you might have come across something peculiar, in your cellar perhaps, that might verify the truth of the rumour."

"Well, I'm sorry to disappoint you, Your Highness. The cellar floor is solid concrete and while there may have once been a trap door or some sort of contraption, I can assure you that it no longer exists. I was down there only the other day cataloguing my collection of vintage wines and if there was a trap door I would have surely stumbled upon it by now."

Prince Charles reluctantly accepted this disappointing news and we moved on to other subjects. After a rather intense debate about the relative merits of milk I developed a rather nasty headache and informed my host that I really should be making my way home. Prince Charles kindly phoned me a mini-cab and I was back in my ground-floor mansion flat before midnight. I felt slightly bad about lying to the heir to the throne but I reckoned he was probably used to it.

How many lies had I told him exactly? Three, to be precise. I had never been down to the cellar in my life. I have never collected vintage wine and I didn't have a severe headache. But if there was a tunnel I certainly wasn't going to share it with anyone, let alone Prince Charles. I wasted no time in dashing home and making my way down to the cellar. To my absolute astonishment

I found a solid concrete floor. What on earth had Prince Charles been wittering on about? And then – ! And then I noticed a tiny red button on the wall, just two inches above the floor. I pressed it and a section of the wall slid back. I peered inside the hole and saw a narrow flight of stairs heading down into the gloom. I found a light switch at the top of the stairs and turned it on. The stairs were extremely steep and there wasn't much headroom at first. But as I made my way down them the passageway opened up considerably. At the bottom I found a little wooden platform. Running alongside the platform was a narrow gauge railway track. And resting on the rails were three small electric cars.

I climbed into the first one and studied the controls. I found five buttons on the dashboard marked start, stop, forward, reverse and Radio 2. There wasn't much future in reverse because of the two cars behind me so I pressed the start button and headed off down the dark tunnel. Two headlights on the front of the electric car illuminated part of the track ahead of me. After several minutes of travelling in a straight line the track veered to the left and I reckoned that I must be heading out of central London. I passed several little wooden platforms on the way but I kept going, expecting to reach some sort of terminus sooner or later. I'd been travelling for about twenty minutes when I passed a sign reading "West London". Curiosity got the better of me so I stopped the car at the next available wooden platform and got out. I climbed up the steps ahead of me and came to a brick wall. I pushed a button on the wall and it slid back. I walked through. I was in a tiny little room. I switched on the light and recognized it immediately.

I was in Billy Castell's office.

Chapter 6

Well, that was more than enough for one night so I took the electric car home, drank a few brandies and fell contentedly to sleep. I woke up the next morning extremely cheery. Emily left the house early to attend one of her "Abolish the NHS" meetings and I made myself a cup of tea in the kitchen. The previous night's adventure had proved that Prince Charles was right and that he wasn't just a lonely figure of fun living in a fantasy world of make-believe. I'd also discovered how Billy had managed to leave a typewritten note for me ten minutes before my break-in into his office ten years earlier. Clearly he'd been there up to the last minute before escaping through the secret tunnel. I finished the cup of tea and three minutes later I was back down there again, riding my electric car under London. Over the next few months I explored a great deal of the system. I discovered routes that took me to, amongst other places, the Theatre Royal Drury Lane, the Oval cricket ground and the House of Lords. And I eventually found the stairs that led to directly inside Buckingham Palace. For the first time in my life I was truly happy. There was always something new to discover. One day I stopped at a wooden platform, climbed the stairs and found myself inside a pillar

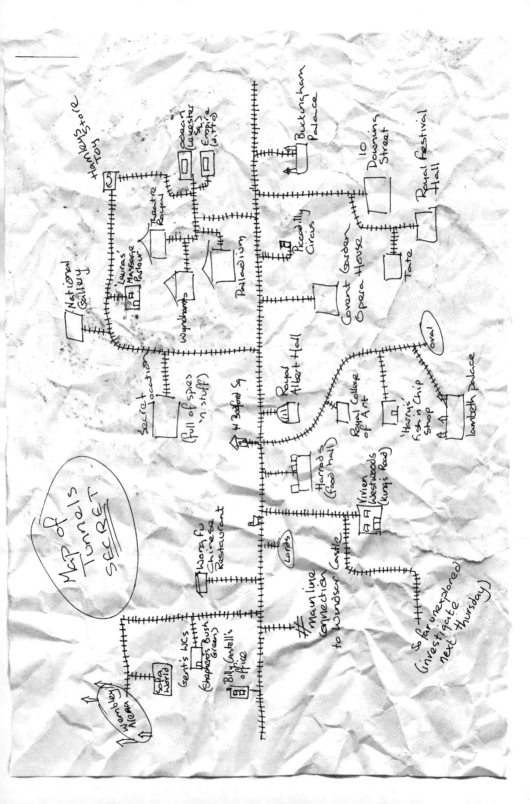

box in Piccadilly Circus. I could see Eros clearly through the slot.

It was with some regret that I re-surfaced to record another series of *Lucky Beggars*. I'd decided early on not to tell Emily about the tunnels because they had to remain secret. That was half the fun of them. She was always out of the house every day so I had ample opportunity to go where I liked. In the summer of 1976 we holidayed in Monte Carlo. I ignored the temptation of the crowded casinos and instead amused myself by being rude about foreigners in a very loud voice. This pleased Emily a great deal and I can still hear her peals of laughter every time I shouted "Monsieur Fat-Arse" at various portly Frenchmen trying to squeeze themselves in and out of open-topped sports cars. It was fun. But on the whole I'd rather have been at home; underground.

At the end of 1976 I was once again voted ITV Personality of the Year. I celebrated by drinking champagne in the centre circle of Wembley Stadium at half past three in the morning. The ITV award meant nothing to Emily and our circle of friends. And this started to bother Emily. I suppose she wanted to be proud of me but this was impossible if my career was generally considered inconsequential fluff and therefore a subject best avoided at the dinner table. In order to please Emily I turned down another series of *Lucky Beggars*. I was sick of it anyway, and instead auditioned for the Royal Shakespeare Company. I knew this would impress her friends and I suppose in the back of my mind was the thought that quiz show hosts never get enough credit in this business so I might as well do something poncy for a change.

But tragedy struck. I didn't pass the audition! Can you imagine that? Still in the end who really wants to spend two years talking a load of mumbo-jumbo to a bunch of people who don't know what you're on about and will happily pay through the nose for the privilege?

Emily of course had told everybody that I was joining the Royal Shakespeare Company and once the news of my failure had got around I became an object of derision – Emily even had the nerve to tell me that I was becoming an embarrassment. I got angry with her and I suppose if I'd been in my right mind I never would have accepted a children's television series.

I can barely bring myself to talk about the horror that was *Uncle Paul and his Happy Hippo*. The first series was so popular with the under-fives that I was persuaded to embark on a nation-wide tour with a fully grown hippopotamus called Augustine. The hippo's speciality was impressions. I'd put a giant pair of glasses on its face while a three-piece backing band played "Don't Go

Breaking my heart". This stupid attempt to represent Elton John was always greeted with such enthusiastic applause you'd swear it must be a perfect likeness. As far as I was concerned the hippo simply stood there creating a hell of a stink but nobody else seemed at all bothered by its lack of miming skills.

I will concede that Augustine had a remarkable range. There was nobody she could do. Maurice Chevalier, Denis Healey, Bobby Charlton, she couldn't do the lot. God knows why but with the right props and right backing music people roared and applauded. You know, in my opinion you can't claim to have experienced all of life's great riches until you've travelled the length of Britain wedged in the back of a transit van with a stinking hippopotamus. It made the musicians who came with us almost bearable.

Uncle Paul and his Happy Hippo was sold all over the world. Children and their parents loved me everywhere. In one sense the programme had given me back the world-wide fame I had always craved. The trouble was I was now known to millions as the man with the hippo. On my own nobody wanted to know but stick me next to a hippopotamus and suddenly I was everybody's friend. Emily, who had never understood showbusiness, began to resent me rather heavily during this period. We had several

arguments along the lines of 'you love that hippo more than you love me' and despite my denials she began to turn against me. She simply couldn't understand why I had to spend two months in Bogota promoting overseas sales.

One night we had a blazing row. She said her friends laughed at me. Although none of them watched much television, *Uncle Paul and his Happy Hippo* had reached such a level of popularity it was impossible to be unaware of the phenomenon. "It's either the hippo or me," she screamed which was a ridiculous ultimatum considering that I was locked into a three-year contract. She threatened divorce which is the kiss of the death in the world of children's entertainment and so with great reluctance, I strangled her with the ribbon attached to my OBE, cut her body into tiny pieces and fed them to Augustine during a live broadcast from the Ideal Home Exhibition at Olympia.

Naturally I was more upset than anybody that my wife had completely disappeared and despite the best efforts of Scotland Yard her body was never found. As a mark of respect Augustine wore a black hat at the memorial service. Getting her to sit in one of the pews was a hell of a job but it did make a great photo-opportunity. Some might think 'what kind of man feeds his wife to an hippopotamus' but those kind of people don't understand the pressures of my business.

*Despite being a hippo, Augustine had the uncanny ability of exploiting
any situation in the name of publicity.*

In 1977 the double act received the highest honour when Augustine and myself were invited to play the London Palladium for that year's Royal Variety Performance. Amazingly, despite my palace connections over the years, this was the first time in my *adult* life that I'd been asked to perform officially before royalty. Traditionally the audience on these occasions can be rather stuffy and slow to respond to the marvellous entertainment paraded in front of them but I was confident that we could win them over.

Nineteen-seventy-seven marked the Queen's first twenty-five years on the throne and so I set about devising a new act suitable for the occasion. We rehearsed for six weeks and by the morning of the big night I was confident we had a show-stopping routine. Well, we certainly stopped the show that evening but not in the way I'd intended. A great deal has been written about that famous night, much of it false. So here, for the last time, is what really happened.

The trouble started just before we went on when Augustine for some unknown reason suddenly took an intense dislike to Bruce Forsyth. This created a massive problem for the rest of the evening because Bruce was compering and could hardly be expected to skulk around backstage all night trying to avoid an angry hippopotamus.

We had been given number three dressing-room which was a bit of a tight squeeze because we were sharing with Gloria Gaynor and Frankie Vaughn. However, we all mucked in together, particularly Augustine, and at first there didn't seem to be any cause for concern.

We were billed to follow some Hungarian violinists and so watched the last half of their act from the wings. Bruce tapped me on the shoulder and wished me luck. At the sound of his voice Augustine suddenly reared and head-butted Bruce in the stomach. The force of a three-and-a-half-ton hippo hitting him amidships sent Bruce careering backwards and into a bunch of Spanish acrobats practising their human pyramid routine. They collapsed like a pack of cards with the poor fellow on top landing on Bill Haley and his Comets. Their drummer took great exception to this and swung a punch at one of the acrobats, missing him completely but catching Bob Hope full in the mouth. This incensed the rest of the American contingent backstage and within seconds a huge fight had broken out with Sammy Davis Junior in particular throwing punches left, right and centre.

Bruce, being the ultimate professional that he is, attempted to restore order but as soon as Augustine heard his voice she charged again forcing him to hurriedly shin up a nearby rope. Unfortunately the rope was attached to a

Established 1976   No 22   13 September 1977

Daily News

Vote Tory

10p

Tragic Royal Fiasco is Paul Mertons Fault

"Paul Merton should be beheaded for last nights Royal fiasco".

This is the candid statement this paper has been given by a high-ranking member of the Royal family who cannot be named since she is the Queen's mother.

What started out as a brilliant evening's entertainment was ruined by Paul Merton and his performing hippo. It would seem that either Paul or the hippo started the fight which was not only seen by the assembled audience as the family – but also by 9,000,000 viewers watching the performance live around the globe.

Of the superstars taken to the surrounding hospital's emergency wards, all but fourteen have now been allowed home. Doctors are especially concerned for Larry Hagman's left ear which was badly mauled. No one has yet admitted responsibilty but dental records are to be checked by the police.

Meanwhile criminal proceedings against Billy Connelly are going ahead. The burley Scottish comedian is said to

Max Bygraves: said to now be in a stable condition and likely to recover the use of most of his upper torso.

report that the wartime sweetheart and singer of classics such as "We'll Meet Again" and "There'll Be Blue Birds Over The White Cliffs of Dover" was innocent of any accusations made to her by Connelly, that didn't apparently stop the hairy scotsman from putting her in a *headlock* and then a *Full Nelson*.

Luckily for the Daily News our regular theatrical correspondent for the evening was joined by popular wrestling contender, Giant Haystacks. Giant reported

Bruce Forsythe and Sammy Davis Jnr: writs have been issued, but the case is not likely to get to court until next June.

that, "Frankly I was proud to be British that night. You'd be lucky to see a ruck of such quality on a Saturday afternoon at the King's Hall in Herne Bay. My thanks go to Paul Merton for a fabulous night's entertainment.

But the stocky wrestler was alone in his praise and this morning it was revealed that Paul Merton has been officially blacklisted for life by the Palladium and the Variety Club of Great Britain.

The Variety Club committee issued the following

Paul Merton: a slow, painful death is too good for him.

statement.

"We were pleased to welcome Paul Merton into our happy ranks some years ago, especially after his sterling fund-raising efforts for Blind Dogs for the Guides.

"But last night's hippo disaster has meant that we have had to re-consider his membership. As from today, Paul Merton is no longer a member of the Royal Variety Club of Great Britain. In fact, if any of us so much as see him I wouldn't give him much more than twenty minutes life expectancy."

Vera Lynn: quoted as saying that whoever broke her nose is 'gonna get it'.

Mr Merton was not available for comment.

Goldfish Threatened by Drought

By Clare Hulton, Senior Drought Correspondent

In a shock announcement yesterday, the Government has declared a water-for-goldfish ban as part of its most recent drought-beating initiative.

With temperatures well into the nineties, top gold fish experts believe that "it will only be a few days before the water in gold fish bowls has evapoated causing the death of hundreds of little golden fish".

"It's a tragic day for fairgrounds," declared Throw-The-Hoop-Over-The-Bottle stall owner, Humphrey Price.

"Who is going to visit my stall and others like it if they can't win a live gold fish?"

And the problem is not just restricted to gold fish. Although their pools will still be supplied with water, dolphins at Brishton's SeaWorld complain they haven't had a drink in days. A spokesman said, "If it wasn't for their superior mental capacity, they would have died days ago."

piece of scenery and Bruce's weight on the rope brought the piece of scenery crashing down behind the Hungarian violinists who were still on stage desperately trying to drown out the noise with a spirited rendition of "Moonlight Becomes You". Now with no scenery behind them, the entire audience, including the Royal Family, could see the assembled cast knocking seven bells out of each other. Billy Connolly had Vera Lynn in a headlock while Larry Hagman and Max Bygraves were giving Julio Iglesias a right pasting. And while this ugly public brawl was happening all around me I stood in the centre of the stage looking out at the trau-matised faces in the audience. What should have been a crowning point of my career had instead quickly disinte-grated into one of the most shameful episodes in the entire history of showbusiness. And people were going to blame me. And they certainly did.

The newspapers the next day were full of it. 'Madman Merton's Hippo Causes Right Royal Rumpus' was how the Daily Telegraph reported it, so you can imagine what the tabloid headlines were like. Perhaps I should stress that none of this was Billy Castell's fault. I had signed up with the Uncle Paul and his Happy Hippo show without consulting him and as always when I took on something under my own initiative it sooner or later proved to be a complete disaster. To avoid any further exposure to the scandal I decided to go underground, which thanks to my knowledge of the secret tunnels was a fairly simple matter. Because I'd embarrassed the Queen during her jubilee year I was shunned by all my high-society friends anyway.

With no one to talk to I happily returned to my electric car. I barely saw daylight for the next eighteen months but I was happy. I discovered a tunnel that led directly into Harrod's food hall so I was always well fed. I had my pick of live entertainment, popping up in the back of West End theatres and cinemas whenever the fancy took me. Sometimes I walked around the Prime Minister's office in Downing Street at 3.30 in the morning. I can't tell you how wonderful it was going where I pleased and never seeing anyone. It felt like London belonged to me.

By mid-1979 it was reasonably safe to show my face in public again. In my absence Augustine had teamed up with a song-and-dance man and together they recorded several hit records. These were so successful that people soon forgot all about *Uncle Paul* and I was able to walk around unmolested. I celebrated my fiftieth birthday on 25th October 1980. I drank a bottle of cheap wine, made myself a cheese and pickle sandwich and spent the evening watching other people on television.

Chapter 7

During the early eighties I awoke to the nagging realisation that as much as I loved the tunnels I still needed the public to recognise how wonderful I was. But I couldn't get work anywhere. George Orwell wrote a nightmarish novel called 1984 but if he'd been me living in that year he really would have had something to complain about. As a creative artist I felt the need to go back to work. Not only for myself but also for my public. Sometimes the public don't know what they want and at that time they didn't know they wanted me. Fashion was against me, Alternative Comedy was the rage. For a while anybody over the age of puberty was considered redundant. There seemed little point in contacting Billy Castell and he clearly saw no point in contacting me. Although only in my mid-fifties I felt my creative life was over.

I was walking through Soho late one evening wondering whether I should walk home or take the electric car when I found myself standing outside a place called The Comedy Store. For those of you who don't know, it's a miserable little basement in the centre of London managed by some very shady people. The Comedy Store is where spotty young performers shout and swear at the audience and some of them even manage the difficult skill of doing both at the same time. Watching the show was a loathsome experience. Afterwards one of the adolescent comics spotted me at the bar and I allowed him to buy me a drink. Much to my surprise he told me that I was a big hero to comedians of his generation. Apparently, by wrecking the 1977 Royal Variety Performance I had struck an early blow for Alternative Comedy! Lots of young people had been inspired to become performers because of this one deliberate act of anarchy. At least that's how they saw it. I decided not to disillusion him by blaming it on the hippo. I thanked him for his kind words and went home to think.

The next morning I placed an advert in *Dalton's Weekly*. A week later I received a telephone call from a producer who was putting together a television show called *Shut up I'm Talking!* He wanted to know if I had a stand-up act and would I be prepared to do three minutes the following Friday? "Of course," I lied. I'd never done stand-up comedy in my life but I reasoned that there couldn't be much to it, otherwise the pimply youths I'd seen giving it a go would never have got away with it. On the night of the recording I forgot my words and fell over the microphone stand. Out of frustration I swore a couple of times which for some reason the audience found hilarious. I waited for the floor manager to give me the go-ahead for a second take but to my astonishment he waved me off the stage and the compere came back on. It took me a moment to realise that I'd just taken part in a *live* television show. And far from being a disaster as I'd thought, everybody liked it. The producer said that somebody of my generation swearing at the audience was exactly what he was looking for and could I come back next week? I made some acid comment about having to learn some new swear words because I didn't like to repeat material but the remark went completely over his head.

The next morning I was front-page news again. It seemed that half the country was appalled by my disgusting behaviour but everyone under thirty thought I was a genius. I was back on the show the following week. This time I rehearsed properly. I'd noticed that the other performers on the show tended to describe real events from their own lives in what they presumably assumed was a comic fashion. I did three minutes about tunnels under London. Nobody laughed. So as a finale I swore at the audience and once again came off to tumultuous applause.

I felt I was on my way back to the top. The next morning the most extraordinary thing happened. I received a telephone call from somebody claiming to be Billy Castell's secretary.

"Mr Castell would like to see you today and wondered if eleven-thirty would suit you," said the female voice on the other end of the line. I confirmed that 11.30 would be fine.

"Mr Castell informs me that you have his office address and that he looks forward to meeting you." The line went dead. Although I'd been businesslike on the phone I could barely contain my excitement. I was about to meet the old man at last. He'd first represented my father in the 1920s so at the very least Billy had to be in his eighties.

Perhaps he was dying and wanted to meet one of his more successful acts before finally fading away. I knocked on the door of 34b at exactly 11.30. A sharp-suited young man in his thirties opened the door and invited me in. "Hello, I'm Billy Castell," he said. "Shall we go for a ride?" He pressed the switch on the wall, we went down the stairs and climbed into an electric car.

"You're Billy Castell?" I said as we headed for central London.

"I'm Billy Castell," he replied. I resented the young man for two reasons; first, I didn't like being lied to, but more important, I wasn't going to enjoy much the experience of sharing an electric car in my tunnel. For the rest of the journey I gave him the silent treatment. After twenty-five minutes we stopped at a wooden platform. I'd passed it many times before but because there was no sign indicating its precise location I'd never bothered to stop off and have a look. We climbed the stairs, the wall slid back and the two of us were standing in a large, well-decorated office. A middle-aged man entered the room, shook my hand and introduced himself. "Hello, I'm Billy Castell." I had an overwhelming urge to punch him full in the face which I somehow managed to suppress. Instead I sat down. The middle-aged "Billy" was the first to speak. "We have a problem with your comic turn on television last night."

"So, write a letter to the Radio Times."

"Billy" ignored my sarcasm and continued. "Your routine about tunnels under London was most unfortunate. We really can't afford to give them any publicity. We don't want thousands of people looking for them now,

BILLY CASTELL (127)

Theatrical Agent
(Secret Agent)

Telephone: Whitehall 1516

do we? If the tunnels are exposed they would have to conform to all kinds of fire regulations and safety standards and probably the entire operation would be forced to close down."

"I understand what you're saying," I replied. "Now tell me why you're both called Billy Castell?"

The two men looked at each other and after some hesitation the following story emerged.

In the early 1920s a young theatrical agent called Billy Castell spotted a heavily disguised King George V entering a luxury ground-floor flat behind the British Museum. The flat I now lived in. Intrigued by the King's odd appearance Billy waited several hours for him to re-emerge without success. Eventually he knocked on the front door which hadn't been closed properly and it swung open. Billy searched all the rooms, which were completely bare and then made his way down to the cellar. As the front door was the only exit to the flat, Billy knew there had to be a secret passageway to explain the King's mysterious disappearance. He found it, and just like I had done some fifty years later, he explored the secret tunnels until he eventually emerged into the tiny little office behind the Goldhawk Road. He established that the office was for rent and so made it his base. I interrupted the story at this point.

*Over the years I have collected these photos, and more, of people
purporting to be Billy Castell.*

"Yes, but there's so much that doesn't make sense. Why would a theatrical agent insist upon communicating with his acts via Dalton's Weekly?"

The older "Billy" picked up the tale. Apparently Billy was travelling through the tunnel one evening when he nearly collided with George V who was travelling in the opposite direction. The King was extremely embarrassed and begged Billy not to tell the Queen because he'd get it in the neck if she ever found out. Billy being a shrewd man exploited the situation to his advantage. Through the King, he had several top-level meetings with various high-up members of the government. In exchange for his right to use the tunnels Billy would work hand-in-hand with the establishment to control various showbusiness personalities whose prime function was to keep the public's mind off the horrible realities of everyday life. And so King George V had been happy to rehearse with Baby Paul all those years ago because he was helping to create a new star, who would stop people rebelling during the awful years of the Depression. I'd been Billy's first big success and so in gratitude many years later he'd arranged for me to buy the luxury ground-floor flat behind the British Museum. As it turned out of course this had been a mistake. Once Prince Charles had told me about the tunnels everything else unravelled from there. And as long as Billy remained a highly secretive figure no one could ever question his motives or strange business practice.

Of course I was absolutely dumbstruck by this news. The idea that my career, my creative art, added up to nothing more than keeping the public in some sort of a happy trance filled me with rage. And I told them so.

"Yes, but what you don't realise," said the younger Billy, "is that you, well, don't have any talent."

I jumped to my feet and screamed at him. "No talent! If I've got no talent why was I ITV Personality of the Year on two separate occasions? Answer that if you can."

The older "Billy" spoke. "I have been authorised by the British Government to officially inform you that you are and always have been a third-rate music hall act."

"How dare you?" I was absolutely livid. "The real Billy Castell would never have spoken to me like that."

"The real Billy Castell tragically died over twenty years ago," said the older man. "In very unfortunate circumstances. But the system worked well so we kept it going. We are just two Billy Castells. There's been dozens over the years."

"Ah yes, but you've made a big mistake, haven't you," I said. "There's nothing to stop me telling the world about you two and your ridiculous schemes."

The younger Billy spoke. "You never really had much

luck with your wives, did you? One down a tin mine in Truro, another one fed to a hippopotamus . . ."

"All right," I interrupted. "But you can't say I haven't got talent. You can't say that. You don't get to where I am, mate, without being a personality."

The two Billys exchanged a glance and the older one spoke. "It is true, you know. And you did say you wanted the truth. Any success you've had has been entirely due to Billy. Sometimes you've had a bit of good luck but generally speaking when left to your own devices, you have failed miserably."

I started to argue back but then realised he was right. I suppose I'd known it myself for years. Whenever I took a job without first consulting Billy it was a disaster.

"So what happens now?" I said.

"Well," said the older Billy, "if you ever mention the tunnels again or repeat anything you've learnt today I'm afraid the police will be asked to investigate the many disappearances that have blighted your domestic life. We could kill you, of course, but that's hardly British."

"You don't have to, mate." I said, quickly jumping to my feet. "I don't need this country, I could work anywhere. I could be an international star if I wanted to. I've done it before, I can do it again. Perhaps you're right, maybe I haven't got any talent but I've got something far more valuable. I'm a personality and that's what people love. I'll work abroad somewhere. When I'm hosting the Eurovision Song Contest in three years' time you're going to look pretty stupid. And some time in the future you'll turn around and say 'Oh, we haven't got any good game shows on telly at the moment' and that's when you'll remember me. And you'll phone me up in France or Spain somewhere and you will beg me to come back and host a Christmas special and do you know what I'll say? Do you really want to know what I'll say? I'll say . . . 'No'. And I'll be saying it with a smile on my face. So when it comes down to it, who's the mug – me or you?"

I flew to Paris the following morning. I left behind me a country that used to be Great Britain. I sold my flat behind the British Museum and eventually settled here in my luxurious Spanish villa.

* * *

Spain was a bit of a shock. Finding work wasn't that easy at first. I compered a few bullfights but in Spain comic songs and murdering cattle don't really mix. In 1990 I got the job I'm still doing now.

I co-host a programme on satellite television aimed at British ex-pats living abroad. The programme is called *Happy Hour* and we broadcast live five times a day from a pub on the Costa del Sol. It's one of those

MONDAY 21

COSTA DEL TELLY

Services start at 4pm

4.00 Hello A word from our sponsors, The Egg & Chips British Pub

4.10 Happy Hour Start the evening on the right footing with everyone's favourite comedy man Paul Morton

5.10 Costa Wildlife Repeat of the beach wild-life programme from last Thursday. Of particular interest are the hermit crabs which have adopted beer cans as their shells

5.45 News

5.46 Weather

5.47 Happy Hour Carry-on-drinking with your best mate and mine, Paul Mertin

6.47 Beach Guide Where's hot and where's not. Well in fact everywhere's hot, but only certain beaches have branches of The Egg & Chips British Pub!

7.15 Happy Hour Time to get out the cocktails, mine's a Sloe Comfortable Screw. Starring, as ever, the fabulous Paul Merlin

8.15 Get Yer Bits Out For the Lads All your favourite drinking songs sung by The Egg & Chips British Pubs all male choir

9.00 Happy Hour Mr Showbiz, Paul Morden, drops all pretence and starts on the neat spirits. Things should start to hot up when todays celebrity, Ron 'Axe Murder' McGregor, joins him for a few neat scotches at the bar. Ron is presently on 'vacation' from the UK

10.00 The Big Movie – Amazon Women vs The Martians This film would have almost been a cult classic if it had been shown at the cinemas rather than having gone direct to video. Following the earlier success of Amazon Women vs The Bay City Rollers, this action packed movie spares no expense in creating a realistic fantasy trip to the far reaches of your imagination

12.00 Happy Hour Join the world's best loved comedian, Paul Berton, for a few bevvies before you hit the pubs and clubs down on the sea front. If still concious after six hours of intensive drinking, he will slur a lot and tell you all how much he loves you

1.00 Live From The Egg & Chips British Pub Through the night fun-n-frolics at one of the branches of the world's best pub. Paul Mekon will be on hand to discuss the comedy business in general and drinking specifically. You'll even get to go to casualty with him for his nightly stomach pump

English pubs that English people like to visit when they go on holiday to get away from it all. Viewers tune in to hear what the latest pub talk is about the news of the day back home. I chat to the barman about football, the National Health Service, women, that sort of thing. Occasionally we ask old Charlie (in the corner, with a Guinness) about the weather. Its a good job and, yes, the drinks are free.

I married my fifth wife, Belinda, out of loneliness, I suppose. She seemed lonely and I felt sorry for her. It's eight o'clock in the evening now and she still hasn't arrived back from Argentina. Its my sixty-fifth birthday today. I was rather hoping she might have made a special effort. There's a bottle of vintage brandy on the table in front of me. I suppose there's no harm in treating myself . . . That's better. I drink a lot of brandy these days. It helps me to get into character for *Happy Hour*. I like to think I'm the best pub bore in the business. If you're looking for a loud aggressive drunk, I'm your man.

Yes, life is good. I don't miss England, I don't miss the weather. I do miss the tunnels though. They were happy times. I could go where I liked, nobody looking at me. Away from it all. Independent of the world . . . another glass, I think . . . Mum, I've spent the day dictating these memoirs into a portable tape recorder. When I've finished

I'll send you the tape – perhaps you can get it published somewhere. If you can get it published, make sure they leave nothing out. Not a single word. Come over for Christmas and let me know how you get along. It'll be great to see you. Dad – we could stir a bucket of water – just for old times' sake.

When the book is published it'll show whoever Billy Castell is these days that you can't muck around with Baby Paul. No talent, that's a laugh. I've got more talent in my entire body than most people have in their little finger. More brandy for me . . .

Bastards! If it wasn't for me the television game show wouldn't be a legitimate form of twentieth-century art. I've made my mark. All in all it's been a mixed bag. And talking of mixed bags, where the hell is she? All I ask is she remembers my birthday and that she loves me. I suppose none out of two isn't bad. Admittedly there's a few murders in this book but I think people will forgive me. They *love* me, people do. Anyway there's no extra-diction – *extra-dition* treaty between Britain and Spain so stuff the lot of them. It stuff oh. Ha Ha. Right, just one more brandy . . . I can hear a car coming up the drive. Better late than never. We don't talk much. She doesn't speak English. She insists on talking the foreign rubbish she picked up in childhood. I'm going to bed now. Show her I haven't been waiting up for her. She'll see me asleep and she'll know who's the boss.

Quick piccy . . . Woah! these stairs are awkward, mustn't drop the tape recorder, the camera or the brandy. They'll all remember me when the book comes out. I'll have the last laugh . . Now where's that bloody light switch?